FRYDERYK CHOPIN

ETUDES

Op. 10

Urtext

Edited by / Herausgegeben von / Édition de

Roy Howat

Editor-in-chief: John Rink

Series Editors: Jim Samson, Jean-Jacques Eigeldinger & Christophe Grabowski

Piano / Klavier

EDITION PETERS

PUBLISHED BY FABER MUSIC

LEIPZIG · LONDON · NEW YORK

The Complete Chopin – A New Critical Edition
Neue Kritische Gesamtausgabe · Nouvelle édition critique

The Complete Chopin has been developed by leading Chopin scholars John Rink (Editor-in-Chief), Jim Samson, Jean-Jacques Eigeldinger and Christophe Grabowski, plus individual volume editors. The editorial concept for the series is based on two key premises. First, there can be no definitive version of Chopin's works: variants form an integral part of the music. Second, a permissive conflation of readings from several sources should be avoided. The editors therefore identify a single principal source for each work and prepare an edition of that source (which can be regarded as 'best', even if it cannot be definitive). At the same time, the presence of important variants from other authorized sources enables scholarly comparison and facilitates choice in performance. Multiple versions of whole works are presented when differences between the sources are so abundant or fundamental that they go beyond the category of 'variant'. For further details see the Notes on Editorial Method and Practice on p. 53.

Brownlow Yard, 12 Roger Street, London WC1N 2JU

Printed in England by Caligraving Ltd
ISMN 979-0-57701-573-6
fabermusic.com

CONTENTS

ETUDES
OP. 10

First page of Chopin's autograph manuscript (**A²**) of the Etude Op. 10 No. 3, showing a variant tempo heading.
This manuscript served as the *Stichvorlage* for the French first edition, published by Maurice Schlesinger, Paris, in June 1833.
Warsaw, The Fryderyk Chopin Museum, M/192.
Reproduced with kind permission of The Fryderyk Chopin Museum, Warsaw.

Première page du manuscrit autographe (**A²**) de l'Étude op. 10 nº 3 de Chopin, avec une variante dans l'indication de tempo.
Ce manuscrit servit à la gravure de la première édition française, publiée par Maurice Schlesinger à Paris en juin 1833.
Varsovie, Musée Fryderyk Chopin, M/192.
Reproduit avec l'aimable autorisation du Musée Fryderyk Chopin, Varsovie.

Erste Seite von Chopins autografem Manuskript (**A²**) für die Etüde op. 10 Nr. 3 mit einer abweichenden Tempo-Überschrift.
Dieses Manuskript diente als Stichvorlage für die französische Erstausgabe, erschienen bei Maurice Schlesinger, Paris, Juni 1833.
Warschau, Fryderyk-Chopin-Museum, M/192.
Abdruck mit freundlicher Genehmigung des Fryderyk-Chopin-Museums, Warschau.

Third page of Chopin's autograph manuscript (**A²**) of the Etude Op. 10 No. 3 (bars 46–67).
Reproduced with kind permission of The Fryderyk Chopin Museum, Warsaw.

Troisième page du manuscrit autographe (**A²**) de l'Étude op. 10 nº 3 de Chopin (mesures 46-67).
Reproduit avec l'aimable autorisation du Musée Fryderyk Chopin, Varsovie.

Dritte Seite von Chopins autografem Manuskript (**A²**) für die Etüde op. 10 Nr. 3 (Takte 46–67)
Abdruck mit freundlicher Genehmigung des Fryderyk-Chopin-Museums, Warschau.

PREFACE

Genre and genesis

Chopin's etudes occupy a pivotal place in a long tradition of keyboard learning pieces, one that took new impetus from the piano's dramatic development around the turn of the nineteenth century. From the late 1780s onwards piano etudes appeared from the likes of Cramer, Clementi, Field, Hummel, Kessler and Moscheles, as well as the pianist-composers Hélène de Montgeroult and Maria Szymanowska.

The gestation of Chopin's Op. 10 is documented from autumn 1829 onwards. Writing from Warsaw to his friend Tytus Woyciechowski on 20 October 1829, Chopin mentions a recently completed 'large *Exercice en forme*'; by 14 November that had become 'a couple of exercises'.[1] Only two autograph dates appear on Chopin's Op. 10 Etudes: 25 August 1832 and 6 August 1832 respectively on early drafts of Nos. 3 and 4. An early draft of No. 9 can be dated to no earlier than October 1831 by Chopin's annotation 'Paryż' (he first arrived in Paris on the fifth of that month).

In autumn 1832 the Parisian publisher Maurice Schlesinger accepted Op. 10 as part of a batch of works forming Chopin's first Parisian publications; parallel editions were arranged in Leipzig and London, to protect copyright outside France. Late in November 1832 Schlesinger listed the Op. 10 Etudes among manuscripts already sent for engraving – only to admit early in February 1833 that he was still awaiting Chopin's manuscript of the second half of Op. 10.[2] By late March 1833 Schlesinger was able to send proofs of Op. 10 to his Leipzig counterpart Friedrich Kistner (as engraving material for the German edition); not until 16 April, though, does Chopin appear to have returned densely corrected first proofs of just Etudes 1–6. (At least one further stage of proof correction was still to follow.) The very short time remaining until publication in early June accounts for editorial problems affecting all of Op. 10, as noted in the Critical Commentary.

Over the ensuing years Chopin performed several of his etudes in concerts or private soirées (Op. 10 No. 4 and Op. 25 Nos. 1, 2, 7 and 12 are documented in programmes or notices); he also played them, in the course of lessons, to Friederike Müller, one of his best pupils.[3] The pieces' lasting place in the concert and teaching repertoire is easily accounted for by their wide range of pianistic and musical challenges, combined with inventiveness of form and expression that constantly diverts attention from the purely mechanistic.[4] In that regard they reawaken the musico-expressive core of major pre-classical pedagogical initiatives such as François Couperin's *L'Art de toucher le Clavecin* or the *Clavierübung* of Chopin's idol J. S. Bach. Their qualities in turn inspired later collections by Skryabin, Rachmaninoff, Debussy (whose *Douze Études* of 1915 are dedicated 'à la mémoire de Frédéric Chopin'), Bartók, Szymanowski and Ligeti. The most extravagant tribute comes from the 50-odd etudes of 1894–1914 by Leopold Godowski, which variously elaborate, invert or combine material and textures from Chopin's.

Form and design

The first of Chopin's etudes has long been linked to the opening prelude of Bach's *Well-tempered Clavier*, also in C major, whose progressions similarly unfold through arpeggio figurations over an expressively melodic bass.[5] (Bars 27–29 and 67–69 of Chopin's etude harmonically quote bars 30–32 and 17–20 respectively of Bach's prelude.) In many of Chopin's etudes the left hand sustains the musical structure, to the extent of implying a distinct study for each hand – notably in Op. 10 No. 8, whose texture is almost inverted in No. 12. Etudes 1–6 and 11–12 anticipate Chopin's *Préludes* Op. 28 by forming tonal pairs of major to relative minor, a pairing made explicit by Chopin's manuscript instruction *attacca* from Etude 3 into Etude 4. Etudes 8–9 also make a tonally connected pair, though Etudes 7–12 can equally suggest two groups of three.[6]

We might also read Chopin's title 'Etudes' as signifying etudes in composition, for Op. 10 reveals a level of compositional ingenuity and suppleness new to his music. Most of the pieces elaborate on traditional 'bar form' (in German, *Stollen–Stollen–Abgesang*), whose second *Stollen* leads or blends into an extended central section, before a condensed recapitulation leads to a coda that elaborates on the opening or recalls the central section's material. Within those patterns, shorter motives and gestures often return unpredictably yet logically. Examples can be seen in Etude 8, whose structure pivots around the harmonic shifts in bars 11, 25 and 71, or in the daisy-chain-like sequences of reprised gestures in Etude 7, including hemiola patterns that link bars 26–28, 40–41, 48–51 and finally bars 54–55 (as in the present manuscript variant). In Etude 3 the unusual structure of the opening phrase, which audibly extends itself bar by bar, has been related to Polish folksong;[7] bars 30–31 and 34–35 then feature a single-bar gesture successively presented in four modal permutations. (A long-established tradition of having bars 34–35 merely repeat bars 30–31 a tone higher, alternating major and minor modes, is a later nineteenth-century corruption.)

Recent years have seen increasing exploration of Chopin's music relative to his near-contemporaries. Besides clear affinities between Chopin's Op. 10 No. 4 and Beethoven's 'Moonlight' Sonata (Op. 27 No. 2), Simon Finlow has observed that the final peroration of this etude quotes a bravura sequence from near the end of Hummel's Piano Concerto Op. 85 of 1820.[8] Other links have been traced with the 24 *Études* Op. 20 of 1825 by Joseph Christoph Kessler (whom Chopin knew in Warsaw) and the *Vingt Exercices et Préludes* of 1819 by Maria Szymanowska, whom he probably also knew. The first and third of Szymanowska's collection reverberate so immediately in Chopin's Op. 10 Nos. 8 and 7 (respectively) as to suggest patterns well ingrained in his fingers. In turn, the texture of Chopin's Op. 10 No. 12 is markedly redolent of the twentieth of Kessler's *Études* Op. 20 – suggesting a more solid foundation for Chopin's piece than the unsubstantiated legend of its having been penned as a frenzied reaction to the fall of Warsaw to Russian forces in September 1831.

On Chopin's own admission, his Op. 10 No. 2 was a ***réplique*** to the third of Moscheles's *Études* Op. 70 (published in 1827), a piece designed for nimble passage of the thumb in chromatic runs.[9] Chopin's etude, whose appearance on the page uncannily resembles that of the Moscheles etude, instead places its chromatic runs out of reach of the thumb. The inherent wit of Chopin's piece is accentuated in a presentation manuscript, on which Chopin notated various offbeats to be sustained or leant on in a playfully polka-like manner (see Critical Commentary).

Performing the Etudes

Chopin's pianistic originality reflects his never having had a specialised piano teacher, his approach to the instrument shaped more by native physical suppleness and sheer talent. The intuitively ergonomic fingerings

---

[1] *Korespondencja Fryderyka Chopina*, vol. 1, 1816–1831, ed. Zofia Helman, Zbigniew Skowron and Hanna Wróblewska-Straus (Warsaw: Wydawnictwa Uniwersytetu Warszawskiego, 2009), pp. 317 and 324.

[2] Zofia Lissa, 'Chopin im Lichte des Briefwechsels von Verlegern seiner Zeit gesehen', *Fontes Artis Musicae*, 7/2 (July–December 1960), pp. 46–57.

[3] See Goebl-Streicher, *Frédéric Chopin, Einblicke*, passim.

[4] Chopin would later isolate the pure mechanics of pianism in drafts for a piano method, left incomplete at his death in 1849; see Jean-Jacques Eigeldinger, *Frédéric Chopin, Esquisses pour une méthode de piano*, 3rd edition (Paris: Flammarion, 2021), also Appendix 1 in Eigeldinger, *Chopin, Pianist and Teacher*.

[5] See pp. 69–71 of Finlow, 'The twenty-seven etudes'.

[6] The autograph *Stichvorlage* (engraving text) of Etudes 7–10 shows them initially numbered respectively 6–9, before being renumbered as published. For Etude 7 this was probably a slip, as the engraving autograph of Etudes 5–6 appears to have originally comprised a pair of bifolios (and Etudes 8–10 a group of four bifolios). Etude 7 might have thus been a later interpolation.

[7] Arthur Hedley, *Chopin* (London: Dent, 1947), p. 143, quoting Helena Windakiewiczowa.

[8] Finlow, 'The twenty-seven etudes', pp. 54–55.

[9] See Goebl-Streicher, *Frédéric Chopin, Einblicke*, p. 199.

that appear in his etudes, as in his teaching, include a penchant for thumbs on black keys, occasional finger slides from black to white keys, and recourse to older harpsichord usage of passing second, third, fourth or fifth fingers variously over each other.

Chopin allocated his etudes only to his more advanced students.[10] Of these, Friederike Müller recounted his most specific piece of advice: 'He bade me practice [Op. 10 No. 1] in the mornings, very slowly. "This etude will do you good", he said. "If you study it as I intended it, it widens the hand and enables you to play runs of wide broken chords, like bow strokes."' Müller adds that the piece does not require a large hand, only a supple one.[11] Her accounts of lessons with Chopin otherwise report his advice to practise slowly, with emotional detachment ['froid'] and an emphasis on physical suppleness, sometimes quietly, sometimes hands separately, using the metronome to ensure steadiness.[12] No original source supports a long-entrenched tradition of playing Op. 10 No. 1 with a loud recapitulation from bar 49; after the notated diminuendo through bar 48, we might sense Chopin effectively saying 'this time quietly'.

Chopin's use of ornaments maintains some habits from the *bel canto* tradition of early nineteenth-century Italian opera, launching trills mostly from the upper or auxiliary note, and beginning melodic grace notes on the beat.[13] Examples of the latter appear in bar 21 of Etude 3 and the autograph variant in bar 50 of Etude 6 (where the grace notes can imply some rhythmic independence from the other voices). Common-sense exceptions, such as the main-note start to the trill beginning Etude 8, are sometimes signalled by fingering that Chopin added at lessons. Other annotations made at lessons include slurs that clarify the note order of arpeggiations in Etude 3 at bars 7 and 8 (see Critical Commentary). Chopin's accents can sometimes be pianistically ergonomic: in the opening passages of Etudes 1, 8 and 12 they may be most usefully read as showing where to 'let the hand fall' (as Chopin taught).[14]

Chopin's metronome indications for Op. 10 are reproduced here with circumspection. The extreme rapidity of some of them (notably in Etudes 6 and 7) raises queries relative to the music's articulation, to Chopin's music more generally, and about factors such as the accuracy of early metronomes. In terms of respecting musical detail, sustainable tempos can be gauged from salient passages such as the closing systems of Etudes 5, 6 and 9, or from the denser textures and rhythms that occur in the course of Etudes 4, 8, 10 and 12 (for which it would be inopportune to slow down). By their nature – and as taught by their composer – Chopin's etudes suggest study at a range of tempos for optimal musical and technical benefit.

Reciprocally, no source of Etude 3 suggests a tempo too slow to convey the piece's indicated two-in-the-bar or to make sense of the opening left-hand accents. (The metronome indication, added only at proof, poses its own oddity by marking the quaver in a piece that implies some agogic elasticity within its crotchet pulse.) We may debate how the piece's printed tempo heading, *Lento ma non troppo*, relates to its manuscript heading *Vivace ma non troppo* (Chopin evidently amended 'Vivace' to 'Lento' at proof stage), but a strong case can be made for regarding both indications as essentially equivalent, one focusing on the crotchet pulse, the other on the inner animation. The tempo heading *Lento ma non troppo* appears again on Chopin's intrinsically animated Mazurkas Op. 17 Nos. 2 and 4; the closest analogy to the etude, though, comes from his Nocturne Op. 62 No. 2, whose *agitato* central section, within an overall *Lento* tempo, features the same syncopated left-hand figurations as the etude, which it also melodically quotes (notably in bar 41).

The fifth etude's opening alternations of *forte* and *piano* – introduced in proofs for the first edition – might again be read as enhancing, rather than contradicting, Chopin's original *leggierissimo e legatissimo* concept of the piece (see the opening footnote variant): on pianos from the 1830s such dynamic contrasts, notably in the treble register, have more the effect of colour variation than of sharp opposition. In bars 83–84 of the same piece, manuscript evidence suggests that Chopin may originally have envisaged the descending octave flurry with both hands an octave higher, a possibility thwarted by the f^4 upper keyboard limit of 1830s pianos (the right hand would have to launch the descent from $g\flat^4$, just off the keyboard). That higher option may now validly be reconsidered, given that Chopin, in the 1840s, made some annotations in pupils' exemplars of other pieces that take advantage of upward extensions in the piano's compass, first to g^4, then to a^4.

In keeping with editorial procedure throughout *The Complete Chopin*, the present musical text is based on a 'best source' for each piece, showing viable variants from other sources around it. In Etudes 8, 10, 11 and 12, which take Chopin's final manuscript as 'best source', the present post-manuscript variants may reliably be read as representing his final intention at bars 94–95 of Etude 8 (give or take a debatable d^2 in bar 94), bars 36 and 44–45 of Etude 10, bars 7, 22, 32, 37–38 and 46 of Etude 11, and bars 14–15 of Etude 12. In Etude 7 we might reciprocally see a musically best version in the manuscript articulation at bars 54–55, provided the accents are adequately supported from the bass. Several variants might have been momentary impulses as Chopin corrected copying or engraving errors at proof stage, such as the pitches in bar 61 of Etude 3, the removal of a left-hand chord from bar 12 of Etude 8 (compare Etude 4, bars 48 and 49), the relocation of mordents in Etude 9 (see Critical Commentary), and the revised accent pattern that opens Etude 10. Such variants can often be read as equally valid in either version.

What now matters most is communicating their musical sense. In 1842 Chopin's pupil Wilhelm von Lenz witnessed a two-piano performance of Chopin's E minor Concerto, Op. 11, in which Chopin accompanied his pupil Carl Filtsch. Lenz's recollection of the occasion and its preparation offers equal insight into Chopin's etudes: 'The pianist must be first tenor, first soprano, always a singer, a bravura singer in rapid figurations. Chopin wanted all the passagework rendered in a *cantabile* style.'[15]

Further reading

Eigeldinger, Jean-Jacques, *Chopin vu par ses élèves*, revised edition (Paris: Fayard, 2006). In English: *Chopin, Pianist and Teacher*, trans. Naomi Shohet, Krysia Osostowicz and Roy Howat, ed. Roy Howat (Cambridge: Cambridge University Press, 1986).

Finlow, Simon, 'The twenty-seven etudes and their antecedents', in *The Cambridge Companion to Chopin*, ed. Jim Samson (Cambridge: Cambridge University Press, 1992), pp. 50–77, 302–305.

Goebl-Streicher, Uta, *Frédéric Chopin, Einblicke in Unterricht und Umfeld: die Briefe seiner Lieblingsschülerin Friederike Müller, Paris (1839–1845)* (Munich–Salzburg: Katzbichler, 2018).

Howat, Roy, 'Making sense of Chopin's Etude in E, Op. 10 No. 3', *Piano Journal* (EPTA UK), 114 (March 2018), pp. 31–33.

The editor expresses thanks for support from the Royal Conservatoire of Scotland (Glasgow) and the Royal Academy of Music (London); for willing help from libraries and librarians (notably the Library of the Royal Academy of Music), and from manuscript owners; and for supportive information and advice from colleagues worldwide.

Roy Howat

[10] Exceptionally, for the technically inexpert Jane Stirling Chopin devised some cuts or technical simplifications in Op. 10 No. 3 and Op. 25 No. 7.

[11] Eigeldinger, *Chopin, Pianist and Teacher*, p. 68, also Müller's letter of 10 May 1840 in Goebl-Streicher, *Frédéric Chopin, Einblicke*, p. 198).

[12] Goebl-Streicher, *Frédéric Chopin, Einblicke*, pp. 184, 351, 355–57 and passim.

[13] For more documentation see Eigeldinger, *L'Univers musical de Chopin* (Paris: Fayard, 2000), pp. 74–76, and *Chopin, Pianist and Teacher*, pp. 131–33.

[14] 'Laissez tomber les mains'; see Eigeldinger, *Chopin, Pianist and Teacher*, p. 30.

[15] Wilhelm von Lenz: 'Uebersichtliche Beurtheilung der Pianoforte-Kompositionen von Chopin', *Neue Berliner Musikzeitung* 26 (1872), p. 282.

PRÉFACE

Genre et genèse

Les études de Chopin occupent une place centrale dans la longue tradition des pièces didactiques pour clavier, qui prit un nouvel essor avec la spectaculaire évolution du piano au tournant du XIXe siècle. À partir de la fin des années 1780, on vit ainsi paraître des études pour piano de compositeurs comme Cramer, Clementi, Field, Hummel, Kessler et Moscheles, outre les pianistes-compositrices Hélène de Montgeroult et Maria Szymanowska.

La gestation de l'op. 10 de Chopin est documentée à partir de l'automne 1829. Écrivant de Varsovie à son ami Tytus Woyciechowski le 20 octobre 1829, Chopin évoque un « grand *Exercice en forme* » qu'il vient d'achever ; dès le 14 novembre, c'était devenu « quelques exercices[1] ». Seules deux dates autographes apparaissent dans les Études op. 10 de Chopin : 25 août 1832 et 6 août 1832, sur les premières ébauches des n°s 3 et 4 respectivement. Une ébauche ancienne de l'Étude n° 9 ne peut être antérieure à octobre 1831, étant donné l'annotation « Paryż » de Chopin (il était arrivé pour la première fois dans la capitale le 5 du mois).

À l'automne 1832, l'éditeur parisien Maurice Schlesinger accepta l'op. 10 dans le cadre d'un lot formant les premières publications parisiennes de Chopin ; des éditions parallèles furent prévues à Leipzig et à Londres, pour protéger les droits en dehors de la France. Vers la fin de novembre 1832, Schlesinger cite les Études op. 10 parmi les manuscrits déjà envoyés à la gravure – pour reconnaître au début de février 1833 qu'il attendait toujours de Chopin le manuscrit de la seconde moitié de l'op. 10[2]. À la fin de mars 1833, Schlesinger put envoyer des épreuves de l'op. 10 à son homologue leipzigois, Friedrich Kistner (comme matériel de gravure pour l'édition allemande) ; c'est seulement le 16 avril, toutefois, que Chopin semble avoir retourné les premières épreuves fortement corrigées des seules Études 1-6. (Au moins une autre phase de correction d'épreuves devait encore suivre.) Le délai très bref avant la publication au début de juin explique les problèmes éditoriaux affectant tout l'op. 10, comme l'indique le commentaire critique.

Au cours des années suivantes, Chopin joua plusieurs de ses études en concert ou lors de soirées privées (les op. 10 n° 4 et op. 25 n°s 1, 2, 7 et 12 sont toutes mentionnées dans les programmes ou les notices) ; il les joua aussi, bien sûr, au cours de leçons, à Friederike Müller, l'une de ses meilleurs élèves[3]. La place durable qu'elles occupent dans le répertoire de concert et d'enseignement s'explique facilement par leur large éventail de défis pianistiques et musicaux, allié à une inventivité formelle et expressive qui détourne constamment l'attention du purement mécanique[4]. À cet égard, elles réveillent le cœur musico-expressif des grandes initiatives pédagogiques préclassiques comme *L'Art de toucher le clavecin* de François Couperin ou la *Clavierübung* de l'idole de Chopin, J. S. Bach. Leurs qualités inspirèrent à leur tour des recueils ultérieurs de Scriabine, Rachmaninov, Debussy (dont les *Douze Études* de 1915 sont dédiées « à la mémoire de Frédéric Chopin »), Bartók, Szymanowski et Ligeti. Leopold Godowski leur a rendu l'hommage le plus extravagant avec sa cinquantaine d'études de 1894-1914, qui tour à tour développent, inversent ou combinent le matériau et les textures de celles de Chopin.

[1] *Correspondance de Frédéric Chopin, I. L'Aube, 1816-1831*, recueillie, révisée, annotée et traduite par Bronislas Édouard Sydow, en collaboration avec Suzanne et Denise Chainaye et Irène Sydow (Paris, Éditions Richard Masse, 1981), p. 139 et 143.

[2] Zofia Lissa, « Chopin im Lichte des Briefwechsels von Verlegern seiner Zeit gesehen », *Fontes Artis Musicae*, 7/2 (juillet-décembre 1960), p. 46-57.

[3] Voir Goebl-Streicher, *Frédéric Chopin, Einblicke*, *passim*.

[4] Chopin devait isoler plus tard les aspects purement mécaniques du jeu pianistique dans des ébauches pour une méthode de piano, laissée inachevée à sa mort en 1849 ; voir Jean-Jacques Eigeldinger, *Frédéric Chopin, Esquisses pour une méthode de piano*, 3e édition (Paris, Flammarion, 2021).

Forme et conception

Depuis longtemps, on a fait un rapprochement entre la première des études de Chopin et le premier prélude du *Clavier bien tempéré* de Bach, également en *ut* majeur, dont les progressions se déploient de manière analogue en figures d'arpège au-dessus d'une basse mélodique expressive[5]. (Les mesures 27-29 et 67-69 de l'étude de Chopin citent les harmonies des mesures 30-32 et 17-20, respectivement, du prélude de Bach.) Dans bon nombre des études de Chopin, la main gauche soutient la structure musicale, au point de suggérer une étude distincte pour chaque main – notamment dans l'op. 10 n° 8, dont la texture est presque inversée dans la n° 12. Les Études 1-6 et 11-12 préfigurent les *Préludes* op. 28 de Chopin en formant des paires tonales du majeur au relatif mineur, relation rendue explicite par l'indication manuscrite *attacca* que Chopin note entre l'Étude 3 et l'Étude 4. Les Études 8-9 forment elles aussi une paire liée tonalement, encore que les Études 7-12 puissent également faire songer à deux groupes de trois[6].

On pourrait en outre lire le titre de Chopin, « Études », au sens d'études de composition, car l'op. 10 révèle un niveau d'ingéniosité et de souplesse dans l'écriture inédit pour sa musique. La plupart des pièces élaborent la « forme *Bar* » traditionnelle (en allemand, *Stollen-Stollen-Abgesang*), dont le second *Stollen* conduit à une longue section centrale, ou s'y fond dedans, avant qu'une réexposition condensée n'amène à une coda qui développe le début ou rappelle le matériau de la section centrale. Au sein de ces schémas, des motifs et gestes plus brefs reviennent souvent de manière imprévisible, mais logique. On peut en voir des exemples dans l'Étude 8, dont la structure s'articule autour des changements harmoniques des mesures 11, 25 et 71, ou dans les marches telles des guirlandes de gestes répétés dans l'Étude 7, notamment les formules d'hémiole qui relient les mesures 26-28, 40-41, 48-51 et enfin les mesures 54-55 (comme dans la présente variante manuscrite). Dans l'Étude 3, la structure inhabituelle de la phrase initiale, qui se prolonge audiblement mesure par mesure, a été associée au chant folklorique polonais[7] ; les mesures 30-31 et 34-35 font entendre ensuite un geste d'une seule mesure successivement présenté dans quatre permutations modales. (Une ancienne tradition consistant à faire simplement répéter un ton plus haut les mesures 30-31 par les mesures 34-35, alternant le mode majeur et mineur, est une corruption ultérieure du XIXe siècle.)

Au cours des années récentes, on a de plus en plus exploré la musique de Chopin en comparaison avec celle de ses quasi-contemporains. Outre les affinités claires entre l'op. 10 n° 4 de Chopin et la Sonate « Clair de lune » de Beethoven (op. 27 n° 2), Simon Finlow a noté que la péroraison finale de cette étude cite un passage de bravoure vers la fin du Concerto pour piano op. 85 (1820) de Hummel[8]. D'autres liens ont été retracés avec les vingt-quatre *Études* op. 20 (1825) de Joseph Christoph Kessler (que Chopin connaissait à Varsovie) et les *Vingt Exercices et Préludes* (1819) de Maria Szymanowska, qu'il connaissait sans doute aussi. La première et la troisième pièce du recueil de Szymanowska résonnent si immédiatement dans les n°s 8 et 7 (respectivement) de l'op. 10 de Chopin qu'on a l'impression de formules bien incrustées dans ses doigts. À son tour, la texture de l'op. 10 n° 12 de Chopin rappelle fortement la douzième des *Études* op. 20 de Kessler – renvoyant pour la pièce de Chopin à une base plus solide que la légende sans fondement selon laquelle elle aurait été écrite comme une réaction frénétique à la chute de Varsovie aux mains des forces Russes en septembre 1831.

[5] Voir Finlow, « The twenty-seven études », p. 69-71.

[6] La *Stichvorlage* autographe (manuscrit pour la gravure) des Études 7-10 montre qu'elles étaient initialement numérotées 6-9, avant d'être renumérotées telles qu'elles furent publiées. Pour l'Étude 7, c'était sans doute une erreur, car l'autographe destiné au graveur des Études 5-6 se composait à l'origine, semble-t-il, d'une paire de bifeuillets (et les Études 8-10 d'un groupe de quatre bifeuillets). L'Étude 7 pourrait donc être une interpolation ultérieure.

[7] Arthur Hedley, *Chopin* (Londres, Dent, 1947), p. 143, citant Helena Windakiewiczowa.

[8] Finlow, « The twenty-seven études », p. 54-55.

De l'aveu de Chopin lui-même, son op. 10 nº 2 était une « réplique » à la troisième des *Études* op. 70 de Moscheles (publiées en 1827), une pièce conçue pour travailler le passage agile du pouce dans les traits chromatiques[9]. L'étude de Chopin, dont l'apparence sur la page ressemble étonnamment à celle de l'étude de Moscheles, met cependant ses traits chromatiques hors de portée du pouce. L'humour inhérent à la pièce de Chopin est souligné dans un manuscrit de présentation, sur lequel il a noté divers contretemps à tenir ou à appuyer d'une manière enjouée qui évoque la polka (voir commentaire critique).

Interprétation des Études

L'originalité pianistique de Chopin reflète le fait qu'il n'a jamais eu de professeur de piano spécialisé, et que son approche de l'instrument était davantage modelée par sa souplesse physique innée et son simple talent. Les doigtés intuitivement ergonomiques qui apparaissent dans ses études, comme dans son enseignement, révèlent notamment un penchant pour le pouce sur les touches noires, d'occasionnels glissements du doigt d'une touche noire à une blanche, et le recours à l'ancienne technique clavecinistique consistant à passer les deuxièmes, troisième, quatrième ou cinquième doigts l'un par-dessus l'autre.

Chopin ne confiait ses études qu'à ses élèves plus avancés[10]. Parmi eux, Friederike Müller rapporte son conseil le plus spécifique : « Chopin me recommanda de la travailler très lentement, le matin. "Cette étude [op. 10 nº 1] vous fera du bien, dit-il. Si vous l'étudiez comme je l'entends, cela élargit la main et cela vous donne des gammes d'accords, comme les coups d'archet." » Müller ajoute que cette étude ne requiert pas une grande main, uniquement une main souple[11]. Ses témoignages sur ses leçons avec Chopin font état par ailleurs de son conseil de travailler lentement, avec un détachement émotionnel [« froid »], en mettant l'accent sur la souplesse physique, parfois doucement, parfois les mains séparées, avec le métronome pour assurer la régularité[12]. Aucune source originale ne confirme une ancienne tradition bien ancrée consistant à jouer l'op. 10 nº 1 avec une réexposition très forte à partir de la mesure 49 ; après le diminuendo noté jusqu'à la mesure 48, on pourrait entendre Chopin dire effectivement : « Doucement, cette fois. »

L'emploi des ornements chez Chopin perpétue certaines habitudes de la tradition du *bel canto* dans l'opéra italien du début du XIXᵉ siècle – lançant les trilles le plus souvent à partir de la note supérieure ou auxiliaire, et commençant les petites notes mélodiques sur le temps[13]. On trouve des exemples de ces dernières à la mesure 21 de l'Étude 3 et dans la variante autographe à la mesure 50 de l'Étude 6 (où les petites notes pourraient supposer une certaine indépendance rythmique par rapport aux autres voix). Les exceptions de bon sens, comme le début sur la note principale du trille qui commence l'Étude 8, sont parfois signalées par des doigtés que Chopin ajouta lors de leçons. D'autres annotations faites lors des leçons comprennent des liaisons qui clarifient l'ordre des notes dans les arpègements de l'Étude 3 aux mesures 7 et 8 (voir commentaire critique). Les accents de Chopin se révèlent parfois pianistiquement ergonomiques : au début des Études 1, 8 et 12, ils peuvent se lire le plus utilement comme indications de l'endroit où il faut « laisser tomber les mains » (comme il l'enseignait)[14].

Les indications métronomiques de Chopin pour l'op. 10 sont reproduites ici avec circonspection. L'extrême rapidité de certaines d'entre elles (notamment pour les Études 6 et 7) pose des questions sur l'articulation de la musique, sur la musique de Chopin plus généralement, et sur des aspects comme l'exactitude des métronomes de l'époque. Pour le respect du détail musical, on peut estimer des tempi viables à partir de passages saillants comme les derniers systèmes des Études 5, 6 et 9, ou les textures et rythmes plus denses qui surviennent au cours des Études 4, 8, 10 et 12 (pour lesquels il serait inopportun de ralentir). Par leur nature – et telles qu'enseignées par le compositeur – les études de Chopin suggèrent un éventail de tempi pour un bénéfice musical et technique optimal.

Inversement, aucune source de l'Étude 3 n'oriente vers un tempo trop lent pour rendre la mesure à deux temps indiquée ou donner du sens aux accents de main gauche au début. (L'indication métronomique, ajoutée seulement sur épreuves, est en soi étrange en marquant la croche dans une pièce qui suppose une certaine élasticité agogique dans sa pulsation de noire.) On peut se demander quel est le rapport entre l'indication de tempo de la pièce imprimée, *Lento ma non troppo*, et l'indication manuscrite, *Vivace ma non troppo* (Chopin a manifestement changé « Vivace » en « Lento » au moment des épreuves), mais il y a de bonnes raisons de penser que les deux indications sont essentiellement équivalentes, l'une se focalisant sur la pulsation de noire, l'autre sur l'animation interne. L'indication *Lento ma non troppo* apparaît de nouveau dans les Mazurkas op. 17 nᵒˢ 2 et 4 de Chopin, intrinsèquement animées ; l'analogie la plus proche de l'étude est cependant son Nocturne op. 62 nº 2, dont la section centrale *agitato*, au sein d'un tempo global *Lento*, présente les mêmes figurations syncopées de main gauche que l'étude, qu'elle cite aussi mélodiquement (notamment à la mesure 41).

L'alternance de *forte* et de *piano* au début de la cinquième étude – introduite dans les épreuves de la première édition – pourrait elle aussi se lire comme renforçant plutôt que contredisant l'indication originale de Chopin pour la pièce, *leggierissimo e legatissimo* (voir la variante du début en note de bas de page) : sur les pianos des années 1830, de tels contrastes dynamiques, notamment dans le registre aigu, avaient plus un effet de changement de couleur que de franche opposition. Aux mesures 83-84 de la même pièce, le manuscrit laisse à penser que Chopin envisagea peut-être à l'origine la rafale descendante en octaves aux deux mains une octave plus haut – possibilité contrecarrée par la limite supérieure dans l'aigu, *fa*^{6}, des pianos des années 1830 (la main droite aurait dû commencer la descente au *sol*♭^{6}, juste au-delà du clavier). Cette option plus aigüe pourrait désormais être légitimement reconsidérée, étant donné que Chopin, dans les années 1840, fit, dans les exemplaires de ses élèves, quelques annotations pour d'autres pièces qui tirent parti de l'extension vers l'aigu du clavier, d'abord à *sol*^{6}, puis à *la*^{6}.

Conformément aux principes éditoriaux de *The Complete Chopin*, le texte musical que voici est fondé sur une « meilleure source » pour chaque pièce, montrant les variantes viables provenant d'autres sources autour d'elle. Dans les Études 8, 10, 11 et 12, qui prennent le manuscrit définitif de Chopin comme « meilleure source », on peut considérer que les présentes variantes post-manuscrit représentent de manière fiable ses intentions définitives aux mesures 94-95 de l'Étude 8 (à un *ré*^{4} près mesure 94), aux mesures 36 et 44-45 de l'Étude 10, aux mesures 7, 22, 32, 37-38 et 46 de l'Étude 11, et aux mesures 14-15 de l'Étude 12. Inversement, dans l'Étude 7, on pourrait voir la meilleure version musicale dans l'articulation du manuscrit aux mesures 54-55, à condition que les accents aient le soutien adéquat de la basse. Plusieurs variantes pourraient avoir été des impulsions passagères à mesure que Chopin corrigeait des erreurs de copie ou de gravure sur épreuves, comme les hauteurs mesure 61 de l'Étude 3, la suppression d'un accord de main gauche mesure 12 de l'Étude 8 (à comparer à Étude 4, mesures 48 et 49), le déplacement de mordants dans l'Étude 9 (voir commentaire critique), et la disposition révisée des accents qui ouvrent l'Étude 10. De tels passages peuvent souvent sembler tout aussi valides dans l'une ou l'autre version.

Ce qui importe maintenant le plus est de rendre leur sens musical. En 1842, Wilhelm von Lenz, élève de Chopin, assista à une exécution à deux pianos du Concerto en *mi* mineur op. 11 de son maître, lors de laquelle le compositeur accompagnait son élève Carl Filtsch. Le souvenir que rapporte Lenz de l'occasion et de sa préparation nous éclaire aussi sur les études de Chopin : « Le pianiste doit être premier ténor, premier soprano, toujours chanteur, chanteur de bravoure. Chopin voulait que toutes les figurations soient rendues dans un style *cantabile*[15]. »

[9] Voir Goebl-Streicher, *Frédéric Chopin, Einblicke*, p. 199.

[10] À titre exceptionnel, pour Jane Stirling, qui manquait de technique, Chopin introduisit quelques coupures ou simplifications techniques dans l'op. 10 nº 3 et l'op. 25 nº 7.

[11] Eigeldinger, *Chopin vu par ses élèves*, p. 99.

[12] Goebl-Streicher, *Frédéric Chopin, Einblicke*, p. 184, 351, 355-357 et *passim*.

[13] Pour plus de documentation, voir Eigeldinger, *L'Univers musical de Chopin* (Paris, Fayard, 2000), p. 74-76, *Chopin vu par ses élèves*, p. 175-177.

[14] Voir Eigeldinger, *Chopin vu par ses élèves*, p. 48.

[15] Wilhelm von Lenz : « Uebersichtliche Beurtheilung der Pianoforte-Kompositionen von Chopin », *Neue Berliner Musikzeitung* 26 (1872), p. 282.

Bibliographie sommaire

Eigeldinger, Jean-Jacques, *Chopin vu par ses élèves*, édition révisée (Paris, Fayard, 2006).

Finlow, Simon, « The twenty-seven études and their antecedents », in *The Cambridge Companion to Chopin*, éd. Jim Samson (Cambridge, Cambridge University Press, 1992), p. 50-77, 302-305.

Goebl-Streicher, Uta, *Frédéric Chopin, Einblicke in Unterricht und Umfeld: die Briefe seiner Lieblingsschülerin Friederike Müller, Paris (1839-1845)* (Munich-Salzbourg, Katzbichler, 2018).

Howat, Roy, « Making sense of Chopin's Etude in E, Op. 10 No. 3 », *Piano Journal* (EPTA UK), 114 (mars 2018), p. 31-33.

L'éditeur remercie pour leur soutien le Royal Conservatoire of Scotland (Glasgow) et la Royal Academy of Music (Londres) ; pour leur aide de nombreux bibliothécaires et bibliothèques, notamment à la Royal Academy of Music, ainsi que les propriétaires de manuscrits ; et pour leur conseils et leurs informations précieuses des collègues du monde entier.

Roy Howat

(Traduction : Dennis Collins)

VORWORT

Gattung und Entstehung

In einer langen Tradition von Klavierübungen gelten Chopins Etüden als ein Meilenstein. Bereits zuvor hatte die rasante Weiterentwicklung des Klaviers um die Wende des 19. Jahrhunderts der Gattung neuen Auftrieb gegeben. Ab den späten 1780ern veröffentlichten Cramer, Clementi, Field, Hummel, Keßler, Moscheles und ihresgleichen sowie die Pianistinnen und Komponistinnen Hélène de Montgeroult und Maria Szymanowska Etüden für Klavier.

Die ersten Quellen zur Entstehung von Chopins op. 10 stammen aus dem Herbst 1829. In einem Brief aus Warschau an seinen Freund Tytus Woyciechowski vom 20. Oktober 1829 erwähnt Chopin eine kürzlich beendete „große *Exercice en forme*"; am 14. November hatten sich daraus „einige Etüden" entwickelt.[1] Nur zwei Datumsangaben finden sich in der Urschrift von Chopins Opus 10: der 25. August 1832 und der 6. August 1832, jeweils in frühen Entwürfen der dritten und der vierten Etüde. Eine Frühfassung der neunten Etüde kann aufgrund von Chopins Vermerk „Paryż" nicht vor dem Oktober 1831 entstanden sein (er traf am 5. Oktober in Paris ein).

Im Herbst 1832 nahm der Pariser Verleger Maurice Schlesinger op. 10 zugleich mit mehreren anderen Werken an, die Chopins erste Pariser Veröffentlichungen bilden sollten. Zeitgleich wurden Parallelausgaben in Leipzig und London vereinbart, um die Wahrung der Urheberrechte außerhalb Frankreichs sicherzustellen. Ende November 1832 setzte Schlesinger die Etüden op. 10 bereits auf eine Liste in Druck gegebener Werke, musste aber dann Anfang Februar 1833 eingestehen, dass er noch auf Chopins Manuskript mit der zweiten Hälfte der Etüden wartete.[2] Gegen Ende März 1833 konnte Schlesinger die Abzüge von op. 10 an seinen Leipziger Kollegen Friedrich Kistner senden (als Stichvorlage für die deutsche Ausgabe); doch erst am 16. April scheint Chopin die ersten Abzüge zurückgeschickt zu haben – mit zahlreichen Korrekturen und zunächst nur für die Etüden 1–6. (Mindestens ein weiterer Korrekturgang sollte folgen.) Dass bis zur Veröffentlichung Anfang Juni nur sehr wenig Zeit blieb, erklärt die editorischen Probleme, die sich durch das gesamte op. 10 ziehen und auf die der Kritische Bericht hinweist.

In den folgenden Jahren brachte Chopin mehrere seiner Etüden in Konzerten oder privaten Soireen zur Aufführung (op. 10 Nr. 4 und op. 25 Nr. 1, 2, 7 und 12 erscheinen auf Programmzetteln oder in Ankündigungen). Im Rahmen seiner Unterrichtsstunden spielte er sie auch Friederike Müller vor, einer seiner besten Schülerinnen.[3] Der dauerhafte Platz dieser Stücke im Konzertrepertoire und im Unterricht lässt sich leicht erklären: Zu ihren vielfältigen pianistischen und musikalischen Herausforderungen kommt der Erfindungsreichtum in Form und Ausdruck, der beständig von den rein mechanischen Aspekten ablenkt.[4] In dieser Hinsicht atmen sie erneut den im Kern musikalisch ausdrucksvollen Geist bedeutender pädagogischer Projekte der Vorklassik wie François Couperins *L'art de toucher le Clavecin* oder die *Clavierübung* des von Chopin verehrten J. S. Bach. Ihre Qualitäten inspirierten wiederum spätere Zyklen von Skrjabin, Rachmaninow, Debussy (der seine *Douze Études* von 1915 dem Angedenken Chopins widmete), Bartók, Szymanowski und Ligeti. Die extravaganteste Hommage an das Werk Chopins sind schließlich die über 50 zwischen 1894–1914 entstandenen Etüden Leopold Godowskis, die das Material und die Struktur der Vorbilder in verschiedenster Weise weiterführen, umkehren oder kombinieren.

Form und Gestaltung

Für Chopins erste Etüde wurde schon früh der Bezug zu Bachs Präludium am Anfang des *Wohltemperierten Claviers* hergestellt. Letzteres steht ebenfalls in C-Dur und entwickelt sich auf ähnliche Weise in Arpeggio-Figuren über einer ausdrucksvoll melodischen Bassstimme.[5] (Die Takte 27–29 und 67–69 von Chopins Etüde sind ein harmonisches Zitat der Takte 30–32 beziehungsweise 17–20 aus Bachs Präludium.) In vielen Etüden Chopins trägt die linke Hand die musikalische Struktur bis zu einem Grad, dass sich daraus für jede Hand eine gesonderte Übung ableiten lässt. Dies ist besonders augenfällig in op. 10 Nr. 8, deren Textur sich in der zwölften Etüde quasi in ihrer Umkehrung wiederfindet. Die Etüden 1–6 und 11–12 nehmen Chopins *Préludes* op. 28 vorweg, indem jeweils eine Dur-Tonart ihrer Entsprechung in Moll zugeordnet wird. In Chopins Manuskript ist diese Paarigkeit durch die *attacca*-Bezeichnung zwischen der dritten und der vierten Etüde explizit hervorgehoben. Genauso bilden die Etüden 8–9 eine durch ihre Tonarten verbundene Zweiergruppe, obwohl die Etüden 7–12 ebenfalls auf zwei Dreiergruppen hindeuten können.[6]

Chopins Titel *Études* ließe sich auch als „Kompositionsstudien" interpretieren, da sein Opus 10 in Bezug auf kompositorischen Einfallsreichtum und Geschmeidigkeit ein in seiner Musik bisher ungekanntes Niveau erreicht. Die meisten dieser Stücke entwickeln sich aus einer traditionellen Stollenform (Stollen – Stollen – Abgesang). Dabei führt der zweite Stollen zu einem erweiterten Mittelteil oder geht dazu über, bevor eine verknappte Wiederholung die Coda einläutet. Letztere führt die Einleitung weiter aus oder greift Material aus dem Mittelteil auf. Innerhalb dieser Strukturen kehren kürzere Motive und Gesten auf unvorhersehbare, aber durchaus logische Weise wieder. Beispiele dafür finden sich in der achten Etüde, deren Struktur um die Harmoniewechsel der Takte 11, 25

[1] *Korespondencja Fryderyka Chopina*, Bd. 1, 1816–1831, hrsg. v. Zofia Helman, Zbigniew Skowron und Hanna Wróblewska-Straus, Warschau 2009, S. 317 und 324.

[2] Zofia Lissa: „Chopin im Lichte des Briefwechsels von Verlegern seiner Zeit gesehen", *Fontes Artis Musicae*, 7/2 (Juli–Dezember 1960), S. 46–57.

[3] Siehe Goebl-Streicher: *Frédéric Chopin–Einblicke*, passim.

[4] Später sollte Chopin die rein mechanischen Aspekte des Klavierspiels in seinen Entwürfen für eine Klavierschule gesondert darstellen, die er jedoch nach seinem Tod 1849 unvollendet hinterließ; siehe Jean-Jacques Eigeldinger: *Frédéric Chopin, Esquisses pour une méthode de piano*, 3. Auflage, Paris 2021, sowie Anhang 1 in: Eigeldinger: *Chopin, Pianist and Teacher*.

[5] Siehe S. 69–71 in Finlow: „The twenty-seven etudes […]".

[6] In der autografen Stichvorlage trugen die Etüden 7–10 ursprünglich die Nummern 6–9, bevor sie dann so umnummeriert wurden, wie sie in der veröffentlichten Fassung stehen. Bei der siebten Etüde handelt es sich wahrscheinlich um einen Flüchtigkeitsfehler, da die autografe Stichvorlage der Etüden 5–6 ursprünglich aus zwei Doppelblättern bestand (und die der Etüden 8–10 aus vier Doppelblättern). Die Etüde Nr. 7 könnte demnach später hinzugekommen sein.

und 71 gelagert ist, oder in den gereihten Sequenzen rekapitulierter Gesten in der siebten Etüde. Diese enthalten Hemiolen-Strukturen, die die Takte 26–28, 40–41, 48–51 und schließlich die Takte 54–55 überbinden (wie in der vorliegenden handschriftlichen Variante). Die ungewöhnliche Struktur der einleitenden Phrase der dritten Etüde, die sich hörbar Takt um Takt erweitert, wurde mit dem polnischen Volkslied in Verbindung gebracht[7]; die Takte 30–31 und 34–35 weisen schließlich eine eintaktige Geste auf, die nacheinander in vier modalen Umkehrungen erscheint. (Eine lange gepflegte Tradition, in den Takten 34–35 stattdessen bloß die Takte 30–31 um einen Ton erhöht zu wiederholen, abwechselnd in Dur und Moll, ist eine Entstellung des Notentexts, die sich im weiteren Verlauf des 19. Jahrhunderts eingebürgert hat.)

In den letzten Jahren wurde Chopins Musik zunehmend in ihrem Verhältnis zu seinen Zeitgenossen und unmittelbaren Vorgängern untersucht. Neben der eindeutigen Verwandtschaft von Chopins op. 10 Nr. 4 zu Beethovens „Mondschein"-Sonate (op. 27 Nr. 2) zitiert der finale Abgesang dieser Etüde nach Simon Finlow eine bravouröse Passage, die sich gegen Ende von Hummels Klavierkonzert op. 85 aus dem Jahr 1820 findet.[8] Weitere Verbindungen wurden aufgezeigt zu den 24 *Études* op. 20 (1825) von Joseph Christoph Keßler (Chopin hatte in Warschau seine Bekanntschaft gemacht) und Maria Szymanowskas *Vingt exercices et préludes* (1819), deren Autorin er wahrscheinlich ebenfalls persönlich kannte. Das erste und dritte Stück aus Szymanowskas Sammlung klingen so direkt in der achten und siebten Etüde nach, dass Chopin ihre Bewegungsmuster in den Fingern gehabt haben muss. Die zwölfte Etüde des Opus 10 erinnert hingegen sehr auffällig an die 20. Etüde aus Keßlers op. 20 – was Chopins Stück auf eine fundiertere Grundlage stellt als die nicht belegbare Legende, er hätte sie als fieberhafte Reaktion auf die Einnahme Warschaus durch russische Truppen im September 1831 aufs Papier geworfen.

Selbst eingestanden hat Chopin, dass sein op. 10 Nr. 2 eine *réplique* auf das dritte Stück in Moscheles' *Études* op. 70 darstellt. Dessen 1827 veröffentlichtes Klavierstück soll die Geläufigkeit des Daumens in chromatischen Läufen fördern.[9] Wenngleich Chopins Etüde der von Moscheles im Notenbild unheimlich ähnlich sieht, sind die chromatischen Läufe bei Chopin eben gerade nicht mit dem Daumen spielbar. Der Chopins Stück inhärente Witz wird in einem als Geschenk präsentierten Manuskript noch unterstrichen: Chopin notiert darin mehrere unbetonte Taktzeiten, die spielerisch-polkahaft gedehnt oder hervorgehoben werden sollen (siehe Kritischer Bericht).

Zur Aufführung der Etüden

Chopins Originalität als Pianist spiegelt die Tatsache wieder, dass er nie von einem auf das Klavier spezialisierten Lehrer unterrichtet wurde, sondern sein Zugang zum Instrument mehr auf natürlicher Geschmeidigkeit und ungeheurem Talent beruhte. Die intuitiv ergonomischen Fingersätze, die er in seinen Etüden und beim Unterrichten verwendet, verraten eine Vorliebe für den Einsatz des Daumens auf den schwarzen Tasten, für gelegentliches Gleiten der Finger von den schwarzen auf die weißen Tasten und für einst im Cembalospiel gepflegte Praktiken, wonach der zweite, der dritte, der vierte oder der fünfte Finger auf verschiedene Weise übereinander greifen.

Chopin gab die Etüden nur seinen fortgeschrittenen Schülern zu spielen.[10] Darunter befand sich Friederike Müller, die seinen konkretesten Ratschlag überliefert: „Er hielt mich dazu an, [op. 10 Nr. 1] in den Morgenstunden und sehr langsam zu üben. ‚Diese Etüde wird Ihnen guttun', sagte er. ‚Wenn Sie sie so einstudieren, wie ich es beabsichtigt habe, öffnet sich die Hand weiter und ermöglicht es Ihnen, gebrochene Akkorde zu spielen, wie mit einem Geigenbogen gestrichen.'" Müller fügt hinzu, dass man für das Stück keine große Hand zu haben brauche, sie müsse lediglich beweglich sein.[11] Außerdem erwähnt sie in ihrer Beschreibung der Unterrichtsstunden bei Chopin seinen Rat, langsam und emotional distanziert [„kühl"] und mit Augenmerk auf Geläufigkeit zu üben, bald leise, bald beide Hände getrennt, unter Verwendung des Metronoms, um das gleichmäßige Spiel zu gewährleisten.[12] Keine Originalquelle stützt die fest verwurzelte Tradition, in op. 10 Nr. 1 die Wiederholung ab Takt 49 laut zu spielen. Nach dem bis einschließlich Takt 48 vorgeschriebenen *diminuendo* scheint uns Chopin geradezu zu sagen: „Und dieses Mal leise."

In seinen Verzierungen behält Chopin einige Eigenarten der Belcanto-Tradition aus der italienischen Oper des frühen 19. Jahrhunderts bei. So beginnen Triller meist ausgehend von der oberen oder Nebennote und Vorschläge in der Melodiestimme auf dem Schlag der Hauptnote.[13] Beispiele für letzteres finden sich im Takt 21 der dritten Etüde und bei der Variante des Autografs zu Takt 50 der sechsten Etüde (wo die Verzierungen eine gewisse rhythmische Unabhängigkeit von den übrigen Stimmen implizieren könnten). Offensichtliche Ausnahmen von dieser Regel, wie den von der Hauptnote ausgehenden Triller zu Beginn der achten Etüde, zeigte Chopin bisweilen durch im Unterricht hinzugefügte Fingersätze an. Unter den weiteren Anmerkungen aus seinen Unterrichtsstunden sind Bindebögen, die die Abfolge der Noten in den Arpeggien der Takte 7 und 8 der dritten Etüde veranschaulichen (siehe Kritischer Bericht). Chopins Akzente haben manchmal eine ergonomische Bedeutung für den Spieler: In den Einleitungen der Etüden Nr. 1, 8 und 12 könnte sie der Interpret als sehr nützliche Hinweise darauf lesen, wohin die Hand „fallen" soll (wie es Chopin unterrichtete).[14]

Chopins Metronomangaben zu op. 10 werden in dieser Ausgabe unter Vorbehalt wiedergegeben. Dass einige davon extrem schnell sind (besonders in der sechsten und siebten Etüde) wirft viele Fragen auf: bezüglich der Artikulation dieser Musikstücke, zu Chopins Musik allgemein und zu Sachverhalten wie der Genauigkeit früher Metronome. Was die Beachtung musikalischer Feinheiten betrifft, so lassen sich gangbare Tempi aus markanten Passagen wie den Schlussteilen der fünften, sechsten und neunten Etüde oder aus den dichteren Texturen und Rhythmen, die in der vierten, achten, zehnten und zwölften Etüde auftreten, erschließen (wo es unpassend wäre, langsamer zu spielen). Durch ihre Beschaffenheit – und ihre Verwendung im Unterricht durch den Komponisten selbst – legen Chopins Etüden für eine optimale musikalische Ausführung sowie den größten technischen Nutzen eine gewisse Bandbreite von Tempi nahe.

Im Gegenzug liefern die Quellen zur dritten Etüde keinen Hinweis auf ein Tempo, das so langsam ist, dass es die angegebenen zwei Schläge pro Takt verschleiert oder eine sinnvolle Umsetzung der eröffnenden Akzente in der linken Hand verunmöglicht. (Die erst bei Korrektur der Druckfahnen hinzugefügte Metronomangabe stellt schon in sich eine Kuriosität dar, weil sie für ein Stück, das innerhalb seiner Viertelschläge eine gewisse agogische Freiheit voraussetzt, in Achteln festgelegt wird.) Über das Verhältnis zwischen der gedruckten Tempoangabe *Lento ma non troppo* zu *Vivace ma non troppo* aus dem Manuskript kann man nur mutmaßen (Chopin veränderte offensichtlich in den Druckfahnen „Vivace" zu „Lento"). Doch es gibt gute Argumente dafür, dass beide Bezeichnungen im Grunde als äquivalent angesehen werden können: Die eine bezöge sich demnach auf die Viertelschläge, die andere auf die innere Bewegung. Die Tempoangabe *Lento ma non troppo* findet sich erneut in Chopins intrinsisch bewegten Mazurkas op. 17 Nr. 2 und 4. Die engste Parallele zu dieser Etüde lässt sich aber im Nocturne op. 62 Nr. 2 feststellen, denn der mit *agitato* bezeichnete Mittelteil in einem an

[7] Arthur Hedley: *Chopin*, London 1947, S. 143, Helena Windakiewiczowa zitierend.

[8] Finlow: „The twenty-seven etudes [...]", S. 54–55.

[9] Siehe Goebl-Streicher: *Frédéric Chopin–Einblicke*, S. 199.

[10] Für die technisch nicht sonderlich erfahrene Jane Stirling nahm Chopin in op. 10 Nr. 3 und op. 25 Nr. 7 ausnahmsweise einige Kürzungen oder technische Vereinfachungen vor.

[11] Siehe Eigeldinger: *Chopin, Pianist and Teacher*, S. 68, sowie Müllers Brief vom 10. Mai 1840 in Goebl-Streicher: *Frédéric Chopin–Einblicke*, S. 198.

[12] Goebl-Streicher: *Frédéric Chopin–Einblicke*, S. 184, 351, 355–57 und passim.

[13] Mehr dazu in Eigeldinger: *L'Univers musical de Chopin* (Paris, Fayard, 2000), S. 74–76, und *Chopin vu par ses élèves*, S. 175–77.

[14] „Laissez tomber les mains"; siehe Eigeldinger: *Chopin vu par ses élèves*, S. 48.

sich *Lento* überschriebenen Stück weist in der linken Hand die gleichen synkopischen Figuren auf wie die Etüde, darüber hinaus zitiert sie sogar deren Melodie (besonders deutlich erkennbar in Takt 41).

Die Wechsel zwischen Forte und Piano zu Anfang der fünften Etüde – erst in den Druckfahnen der Erstausgabe hinzugefügt – ließen sich erneut mehr als Verdeutlichung denn als Widerspruch zu Chopins ursprünglichem Konzept des Stücks als *leggierissimo e legatissimo* verstehen (vgl. die Variante der Anfangstakte in der Fußnote): Auf den Flügeln der 1830er Jahre bewirken derartige dynamische Kontraste besonders in der Oberstimme mehr eine Variation der Klangfarbe als eine schroffe Änderung der Lautstärke. In den Takten 83–84 derselben Etüde lässt das Manuskript darauf schließen, dass Chopin den beidhändigen Oktavenlauf nach unten ursprünglich eine Oktave höher vorgesehen haben könnte. Dies war jedoch nicht möglich, da die Klaviatur der um 1830 gebräuchlichen Instrumente nur bis zum f^4 ging (der Lauf hätte in der rechten Hand auf ges^4 begonnen und dadurch den verfügbaren Tonumfang um genau eine Note überstiegen). Die Wahl der höheren Tonlage darf heute ernsthaft in Betracht gezogen werden; immerhin fügte Chopin in den 1840ern für andere Stücke einige Anmerkungen in den Ausgaben seiner Schüler hinzu, die den größeren Tonumfang des Klaviers nach oben nutzen, zunächst bis zum g^4, dann bis zum a^4.

Im Einklang mit der editorischen Praxis dieser Gesamtausgabe basiert der vorliegende Notentext auf einer „zuverlässigsten Quelle“ für jedes Stück, enthält jedoch vertretbare Varianten, die aus weiteren verwandten Quellen stammen. In den Etüden Nr. 8, 10, 11 und 12, wo Chopins endgültiges Manuskript als „zuverlässigste Quelle“ zugrunde liegt, können die angegebenen, später zur Druckfassung hinzugefügten Varianten für die Takte 94–95 der achten Etüde (mit Ausnahme des zweifelhaften d^2 in Takt 94), die Takte 36 und 44–45 der zehnten Etüde, die Takte 7, 22, 32, 37–38 und 46 der elften Etüde und die Takte 14–15 der zwölften Etüde zuverlässig als letzte Intention des Komponisten betrachtet werden. Als musikalisch befriedigendste Fassung der siebten Etüde dürfte hingegen die handschriftliche Artikulation in den Takten 54–55 gelten, vorausgesetzt, der Bass unterstützt diese Akzente hinreichend. Einige Varianten könnten auf spontane Impulse zurückgehen, denen Chopin nachgab, während er Kopier- oder Stichfehler in den Druckfahnen korrigierte. Dazu gehören die Tonhöhen in Takt 61 der dritten Etüde, die Streichung eines Akkords in der linken Hand in Takt 12 der achten Etüde (vgl. Etüde Nr. 4, Takte 48 und 49), die Versetzung von Pralltrillern in der neunten Etüde (siehe Kritischer Bericht) und die Überarbeitung des Akzentschemas zu Beginn der zehnten Etüde. Solche Varianten können häufig als gleichwertige Fassungen interpretiert werden.

Hier kommt es letztendlich darauf an, ihren musikalischen Sinn zu vermitteln. Chopins Schüler Wilhelm von Lenz erlebte 1842 eine Aufführung des e-Moll-Konzerts op. 11 auf zwei Klavieren, wobei Chopin seinen Schüler Carl Filtsch begleitete. Lenz' Erinnerungen an dieses Ereignis und dessen Vorbereitungen sind für Chopins Etüden gleichermaßen relevant: „Der Pianist hat erster Tenor, erster Sopran, immer Sänger, Bravoursänger in den Passagen zu sein. Chopin wollte das ganze Passagenwerk zu einem cantabile-Styl gezwungen wissen.“[15]

Weiterführende Literatur

Eigeldinger, Jean-Jacques: *Chopin vu par ses élèves*, revidierte Ausgabe, Paris 2006. In englischer Sprache: *Chopin, Pianist and Teacher*, übers. v. Naomi Shohet, Krysia Osostowicz und Roy Howat, hrsg. v. Roy Howat, Cambridge, 1986.

Finlow, Simon: „The twenty-seven etudes and their antecedents“, in: *The Cambridge Companion to Chopin*, hrsg. v. Jim Samson, Cambridge 1992, S. 50–77, 302–305.

Goebl-Streicher, Uta: *Frédéric Chopin – Einblicke in Unterricht und Umfeld: Die Briefe seiner Lieblingsschülerin Friederike Müller, Paris 1839–1845*, München u. Salzburg 2018.

Howat, Roy: „Making sense of Chopin's Etude in E, Op. 10 No. 3“, *Piano Journal* (EPTA UK), 114 (März 2018), S. 31–33.

Der Herausgeber dankt dem Royal Conservatoire of Scotland (Glasgow) und der Royal Academy of Music (London) für ihre Unterstützung, den Bibliotheken (insbesondere der Library of the Royal Academy of Music) und ihren Mitarbeiterinnen und Mitarbeitern sowie den Eigentümern der Manuskripte für ihre zuvorkommende Hilfe und seinen Kolleginnen und Kollegen in aller Welt für weiterführende Informationen und Ratschläge.

Roy Howat

(Übersetzung: Jan Wolfrum)

[15] Wilhelm von Lenz: „Uebersichtliche Beurtheilung der Pianoforte-Kompositionen von Chopin“, *Neue Berliner Musikzeitung* 26 (1872), S. 282.

Etudes Op. 10

Dédiées à son ami F. Liszt

★ See Critical Commentary.

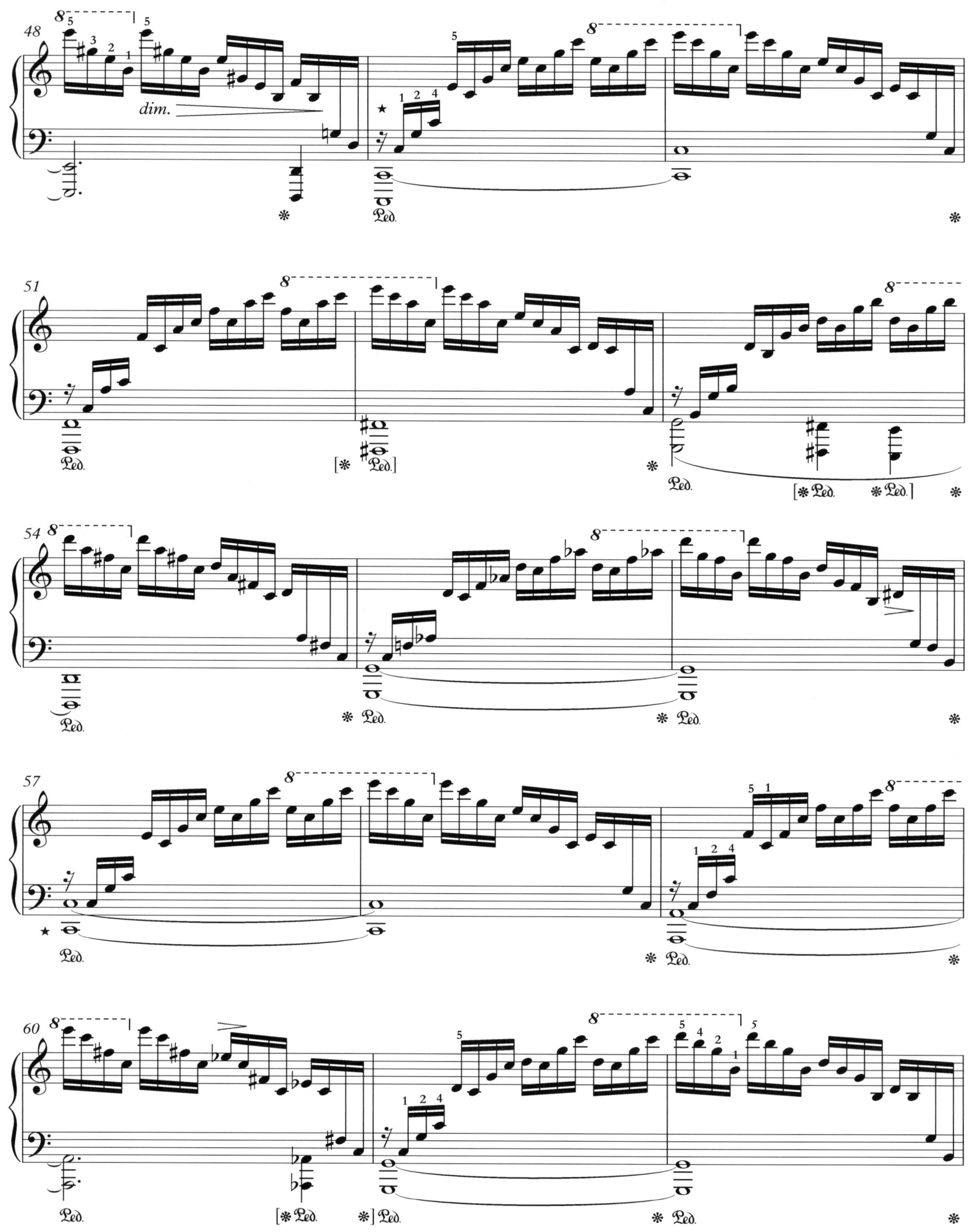

★ See Critical Commentary.

cresc.
dim.

Allegro ♩ = 144
Op. 10 No. 2
sempre legato
2
p
cresc.
F⁰:
3
5
sempre legato
cresc.
7
fz
dim.
9
cresc.
11
F⁰:

★ $C^{1.in}$, A^{1}: ¢

13 *sempre legato*

15 *cresc.*

(*f*)

17 *dim.*

19 *sempre legato*

p

21 *poco*

a *poco*

23 *cresc.*

★ See Critical Commentary.

cresc.
f
fzp
A1:
sempre legato

37
39
41
cre
scen
do
43
f
45
sempre legato
cre
scen
do
47
(f)
dim.

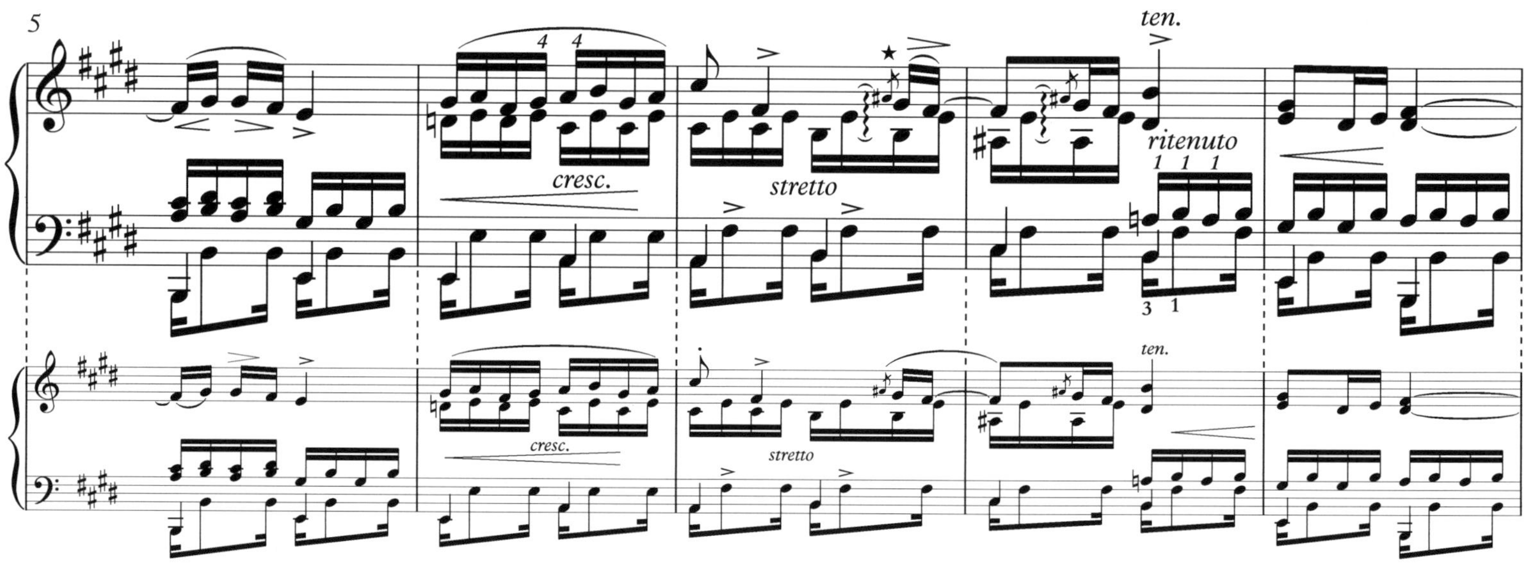

★ See Critical Commentary.

★ See Critical Commentary.

★ See Critical Commentary.

(attacca il presto con fuoco)

Presto 𝅗𝅥 = 88
Op. 10 No. 4
4
con fuoco
f
f(z)p
cresc.
[p
cresc.]
f(z)p
(ff)
f(z)
(A¹:
[meno f]
★A¹: ₵

14
cresc.
f
f[z]
16
18
fz
20
fz
22
fz
G:
A1:
25
fz
f(z)

27
3
3
cre - - - scen - - - - do
29
3
3
31
2 1 3 1
2 1 3 1
33
(A1: ▾)
fz
cresc.
fz
f
2 1 4 3 2 1 4 3 2 1
36
8
f
2 1 4 3 2 1 4 3 2

39
8
41
(
) cresc.
cresc.
43
cresc.
cresc.
A1:
ff
45
ff
con forza
47
fz
p
fz

49
cresc.
fz
51
54
f
f[z]
57
A¹:
60
ff
63
[meno f]

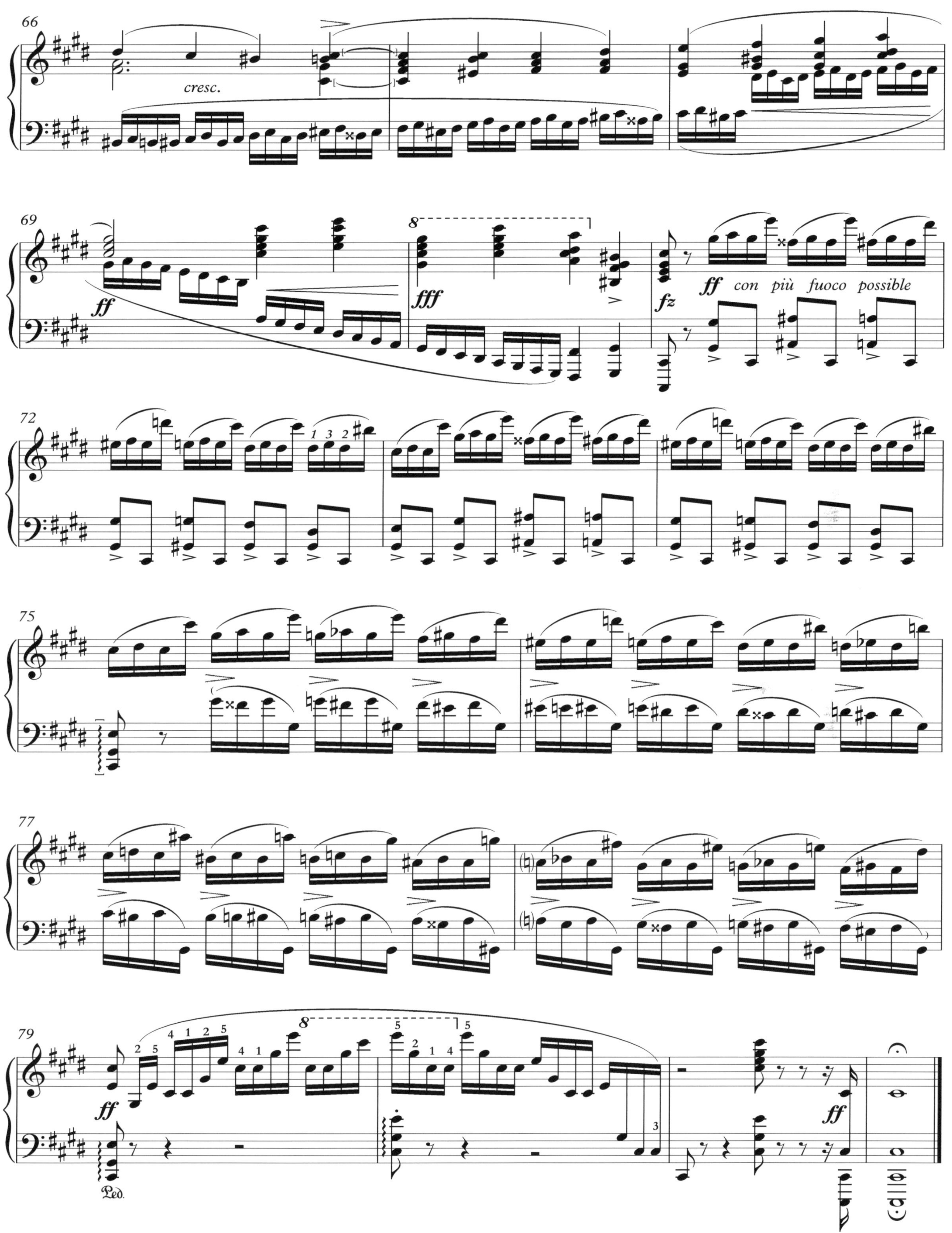
66
cresc.
69
ff
8
fff
fz
ff con più fuoco possible
72
75
77
79
ff
Ped.
8
ff

Vivace ♩ = 116
Op. 10 No. 5
brillante
legato
cresc.
Ped.
poco rall.
a tempo
pp
A²:
leggieriss. e legatiss.
; see Critical Commentary.

★ See Critical Commentary.

37
dim.
41
p
cresc.
45
49
f
p
cresc.
53
f.
p
cresc.
57

★ See Critical Commentary.

★ See Critical Commentary.

19
cresc.
13
4
1
cresc.
21
fzp
legato
(>)
(>)
1
24
p
13
1
27
29
cresc.
stretto
e
cresc.
32
fz

★ See Critical Commentary.

Vivace ♩. = 84
Op. 10 No. 7
7
p
(cresc.)
cresc.
delicato
Ped.

★ See Critical Commentary.

39
cresc.
42
45
A²:
48
51
55
D:
dim.
cresc.
ff
Ped.

Allegro ★ 𝅗𝅥 = 96
Op. 10 No. 8
8
(veloce)
fz
Ped.
(cresc.)
(f)
F, G, E (LH):
★ F, G, E: 𝅗𝅥 = 88

(cresc.)
(f)
fz

29
32
(Ped.
35
(37)
marcato
40
(f)
f
dim.
43

46
cresc.
cresc.
(Ped.
F, G, E:
49
cresc.
(Ped.
(Ped.
52
(cresc.)
(Ped.
cresc.
55
poco rall.
dim.
Ped.
pp
poco
58
a poco [a tempo e] cre
60
scen do
f
(Ped.)
E, G³:

★ See Critical Commentary.

★ See Critical Commentary.

★ See Critical Commentary.

(A²:)

19 *f* *fz* *p*

22 *cresc.* *sempre* *stretto e più*

25 *forte* *accel.* *cresc.*

28 *ff* *f* *pp*

31 *f stretto* *pp* *f appassionato*

34 *pp* *f* *poco rall.* *pp*

37
a tempo
sempre agitato
sempre legato
40
43
con forza
[3]
46
fz
49
cresc.
cre – – scen – – do
Ped. * Ped. * Ped. (*) Ped. * Ped. * Ped. *

★ See Critical Commentary.

Op. 10 No. 10

★ See Critical Commentary.

15
8
f
fz
(Ped.
Ped.
Ped.
F, G, E:
f legatiss.
17
f
cresc.
20
sotto voce
p
23
cresc.
f
26
sotto voce
p
dim.
poco rall.

★ See Critical Commentary.

44
8
fz
Ped.
F, G, E:
cre
scen
47
do
delicatiss.
fzp
50
legatiss.
e
dim.
53
rall.
a tempo
dolciss.
pp
cresc.
56

59
(Ped. * Ped. *
F, G, E:
E:
62
Ped. * Ped. * Ped. * Ped. * Ped. * Ped. *
65
Ped. * Ped. * Ped. * Ped. *) [Ped. * Ped. *]
68
rall.
[a tempo]
dolciss.
sempre
(Ped. * Ped. *
Ped. * Ped. * Ped.)
71
dim. e
leggieriss.
dim.
[*]
74
smorz.
f

Op. 10 No. 11

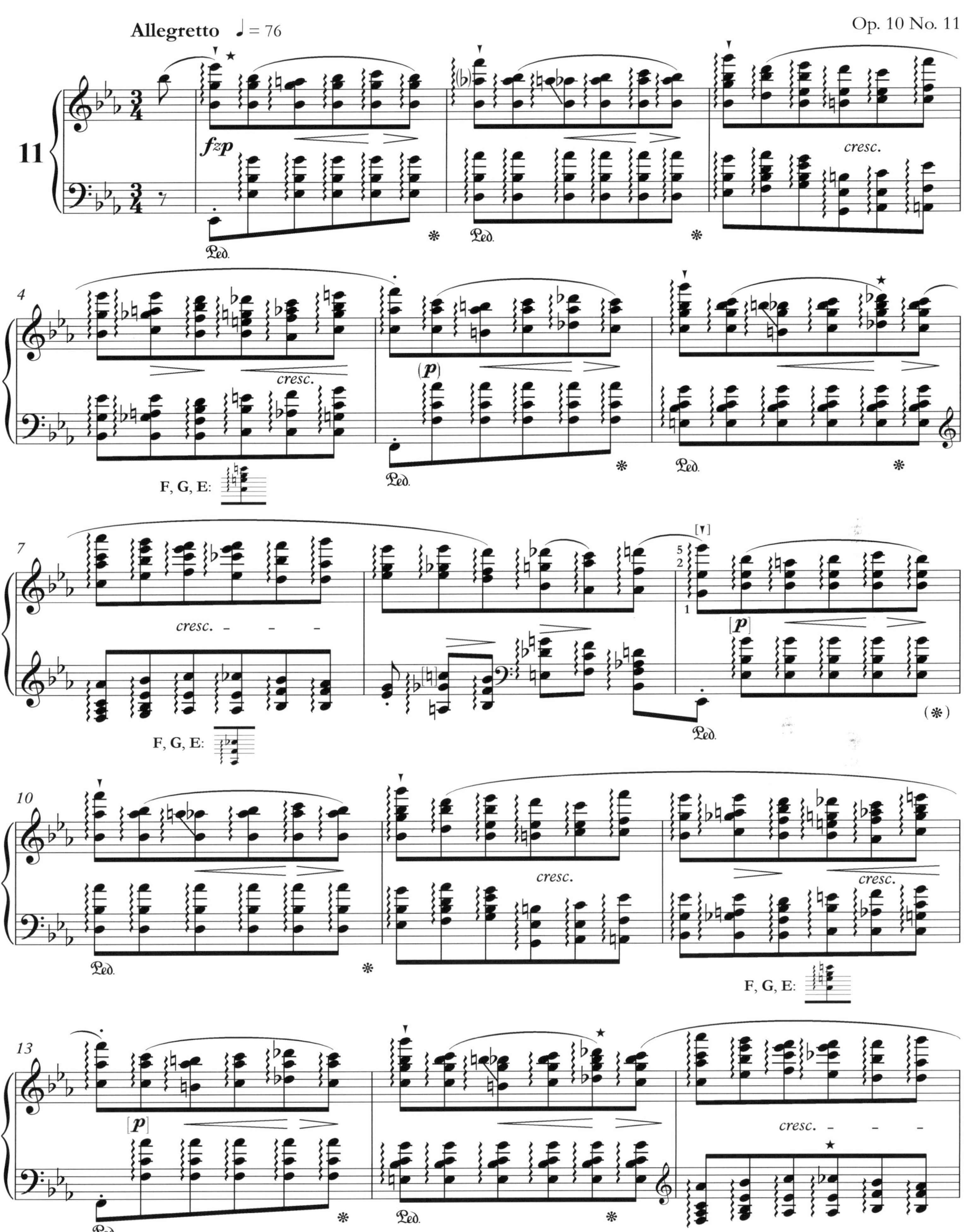

★ See Critical Commentary.

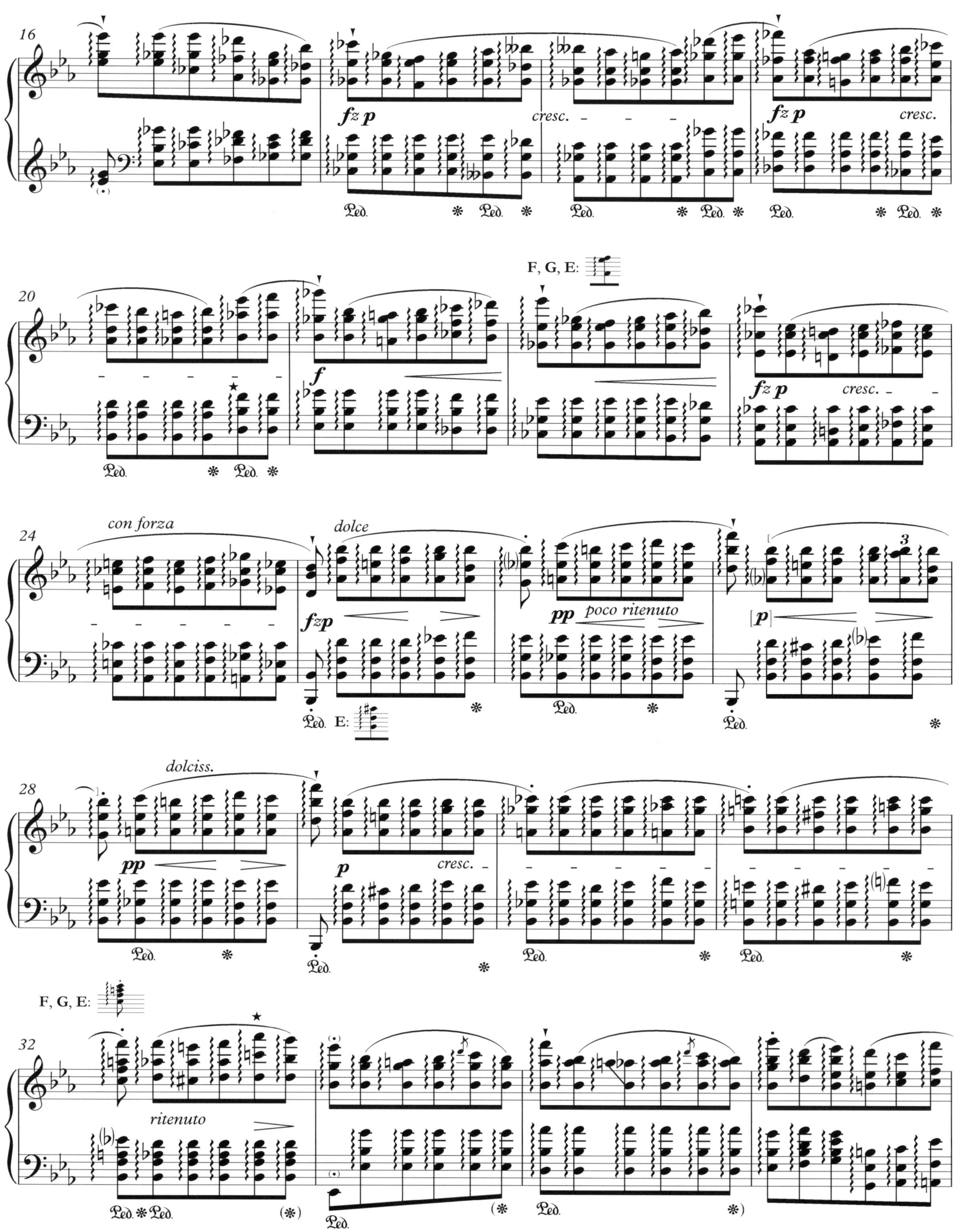

★ See Critical Commentary.

★ See Critical Commentary.

★ Allegro con fuoco 𝅗𝅥 = 76
Op. 10 No. 12
12
energico
fz
legatiss.
cresc.
f
sempre legato
con forza
cresc.
appassionato
p
[p]
F, E:
ten.
fz
con forza
Allegro con fuoco
♩ = 160
★ F, G, E:
bars 2–3
bars 4–5
con fuoco

★ See Critical Commentary.

32
cresc.
F, G, E:
34
cresc.
37
fz
40
ff
43
8
ff
46

49
52
55
58
61
64
cresc.

★ See Critical Commentary.

NOTES ON EDITORIAL METHOD AND PRACTICE

Editorial concept

The Complete Chopin is based on two key premises. First, there can be no definitive version of Chopin's works: variants form an integral part of the music. Second, a permissive conflation of readings from several sources – in effect producing a version of the music that never really existed – should be avoided. Accordingly, our procedure is to identify a single principal source for each work and to prepare an edition of that source (which we regard as 'best', even if it cannot be definitive). At the same time, we reproduce important variants from other authorized sources either adjacent to or, in certain instances, within the main music text, in footnotes or in the Critical Commentary, thus enabling scholarly comparison and facilitating choice in performance. (Conflation may be inadmissible for the editor, but it remains an option and right for the performer.) Multiple versions of whole works are presented when differences between the sources are so abundant or fundamental that they go beyond the category of 'variant'.

Sources

The complexity of the Chopin sources could hardly be greater, given the varying ways in which each work was drafted, prepared for publication (usually in three different countries) and subsequently revised in successive impressions. Our edition takes account of the following sources as relevant:

- autograph manuscripts, many of which were used by engravers (i.e. *Stichvorlagen*, or engraver's manuscripts);
- proofs, whether uncorrected or corrected by Chopin;
- first editions, including subsequent impressions released during Chopin's lifetime if relevant;
- autograph glosses in the scores of his students and associates; and
- editions of pieces for which no other source material survives.

In determining a single principal source for each piece, we have been guided by several factors of variable relevance from work to work. For the music published during Chopin's lifetime, these include the following:

- Chopin's presence in Paris, which allowed him to correct proofsheets and successive impressions of the French first edition, whereas he had less control over the publication process in Germany and England. We therefore tend to privilege the French first edition and later printings thereof;
- the existence of an autograph or authoritative copy related to a particular first edition; and
- the quality of the source with respect to errors and clarity of presentation.

For the posthumously published works, a more *ad hoc* methodology must be adopted, taking into account extant autograph manuscripts or approved copies or early editions when no other source material survives. The rationale for the selection of each work's principal source is given in the Critical Commentary.

Editorial principles

Our central aim is fidelity to the designated principal source except when errors and omissions occur therein. When such errors and omissions are indisputable, corrections are made tacitly in the music text, without distinguishing marks, but are discussed in the Critical Commentary (except for certain types of accidental; see below). When they are open to debate, any changes made editorially are distinguished in the music text by the use of square brackets; the Critical Commentary will discuss and justify these changes as necessary.

When other authorized sources offer significant alternatives, we present these as variants in one of the following ways:

- *alternative music text* is positioned on the page, either next to the main text or in footnotes; the provenance of each variant is identified according to the system of abbreviations defined in the Critical Commentary;
- *alternative dynamics, articulation and other small-scale variants* are incorporated within the music text but are distinguished by round brackets;
- *alternative fingerings* are printed in italics; and
- *alternative pedallings* appear below the staff in smaller type and enclosed within round brackets, their provenance being identified according to the system of abbreviations defined in the Critical Commentary.

Minor alternatives in other authorized sources are discussed and reproduced in the Critical Commentary as necessary, but do not appear in the body of the edition proper.

The principle of fidelity to an early nineteenth-century source raises important questions about the appearance of our Edition, given the differences in notational conventions between Chopin's age and our own. Our general practice is to conserve relevant features of early to mid nineteenth-century notation while modernizing details which otherwise would not be comprehensible to today's performers. The criterion is whether or not a given feature has any bearing on the music's meaning. For instance, we generally follow the original notation with regard to the position of slurs before or after tied notes; the chains of small-scale slurs in Chopin's original texts; superimposed (multiple) slurs; unbroken beamings across multiple groups of quavers, semiquavers etc.; and the disposition of the hands across the staves. We also respect the expressive idiosyncrasies of parallel passages.

Select characteristics of the Edition

- *Square brackets* distinguish all editorial interventions except precautionary accidentals (which are added only when reading accuracy is jeopardized). *Round brackets* (parentheses) designate additions and variants from other authorized sources.
- *Accidentals* missing from the original source are tacitly replaced in this Edition when these are found within the same bar at a higher or lower register, and when they clearly apply to other uses of the same pitch class in that bar (this sort of omission being extremely typical of Chopin).
- No editorial *fingerings* have been added. When Chopin's own fingerings appear in the principal source, they are presented in roman type in our Edition. Any significant fingerings from other authorized sources appear in italics; their provenance is identified in the Critical Commentary.
- *Right- and left-hand parts* may be divided between the two staves when such a disposition is vital to the original sense or better conforms to hand positions. This is how Chopin tended to notate his music, and it may be significant with regard to articulation and sonority.
- *Accents* pose a major problem in Chopin editing. Accents of various sizes are found throughout Chopin's manuscripts (as well as many scribal copies) and apparently have different meanings according to context; nevertheless, such meanings can be difficult to ascertain, not least because of notational inconsistencies on Chopin's part which make the editor's job all the more vexed. This Edition preserves the two principal types of accent in Chopin's autographs: conventional accents (>) and 'long accents' (⟩). The latter seem to have various functions: to indicate dynamic reinforcement, expressive stress and proportional prolongation for notes of long rhythmic value (i.e. minims and semibreves); to convey a sense

of 'leaning' to appoggiaturas, suspensions and syncopations; to emphasize groups of two, three or four notes, as well as rolled chords; and to prolong a stress over tied notes. Long accents are best thought of as a 'surge', versus the dynamic retraction implied by a visually similar diminuendo sign (with which many early and modern Chopin editions alike replace the long accents intended by Chopin). Marcato accents (^, as opposed to >) are retained from the original.

- This Edition presents both *grace notes* (with stroke) and *'long appoggiaturas'* (without stroke), thus preserving a distinction clearly intended by Chopin.
- A flexible approach to *stem directions* on a single staff has been taken. Standard modern practice is not observed when the original stem directions convey a meaning that modernized notation would lack.
- *Liaisons* (i.e. diagonal lines) between the hands are reproduced where relevant; taken from the copies of Chopin's students (especially those of Camille Dubois), these indicate a simultaneous attack on the beat with both hands.
- *Rests* are added only when the original sense is unclear or in cases of error or omission.
- *Pedalling*. Where a 𝆮 marking or pedal release (✻) is either erroneous or absent, and when its placement is unambiguous, such an indication is inserted without square brackets but is discussed in the Critical Commentary; when its placement is open to debate, any editorial correction or addition will be designated by square brackets, with justification provided in the Critical Commentary as necessary. In general, pedal releases are not added at the ends of pieces: the pedalling remains 'open' in keeping with Chopin's practice.
- *Triplets* and similar rhythmic groupings are indicated with small numbers. Such groupings and similar ornamental shapes are not slurred as a matter of policy, as such slurs in Chopin's music often designate legato articulation, not rhythmic grouping. We therefore follow his notational practice.
- Elements in the principal source deemed to be superfluous (e.g. redundant accidentals, pedal releases, slurs, and staccato or augmentation dots) are not retained in this Edition; the Critical Commentary will discuss only those elements which are open to debate.

Critical Commentary

The Critical Commentary identifies the particular strategy for the choice of primary and secondary sources, provides information on sources (including dates and library sigla as necessary) and justifies individual decisions regarding the text. It also reports on relevant variants and corrections of errors and omissions in the principal source. The identification of obvious mistakes and faulty notation in the sources is avoided; so too is the description of secondary musical details in subsidiary sources.

Standard library sigla are given as relevant for manuscript material. The following abbreviations are used when necessary:

RH = right hand
LH = left hand
Br. = brass
Str. = strings
Ww. = woodwind; plus standard abbreviations for other orchestral instruments.

To specify pitches, the Helmholtz system is used as follows:

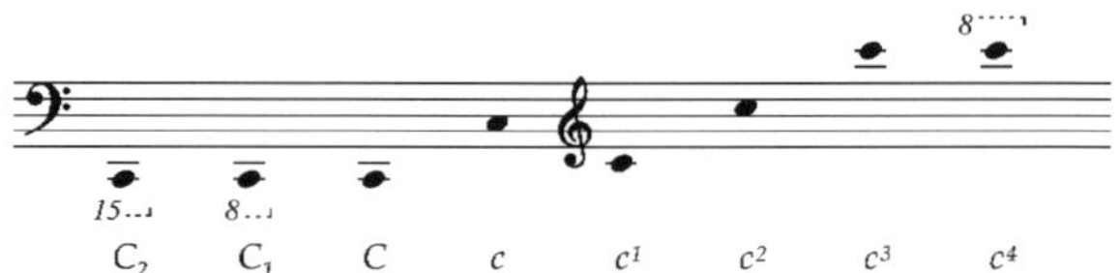

An oblique (/) is used for comments applying to more than one part (e.g. 'RH/LH' refers to both RH and LH). Commas are used in succession when a given feature occurs in a number of bars or sources (e.g. 'Bars 6, 7, 8. > to RH note 2 from **F**') or when a given element has multiple features (e.g. 'Bar 19. ***p***, > to LH chord 1 from **S**').

This Edition employs a precise and unambiguous means of identifying individual notes and chords within a bar. In general, these are referred to in the Critical Commentary with regard to their position as an *event* within a given bar. For instance, in the following music example (the first bar from the E minor Concerto Op. 11):

'w' = bar 1 RH note 3, as it is a single note and the third right-hand event in the bar;
'x' = bar 1 RH chord 4, as it is a chord (i.e. two or more notes) and the fourth right-hand event in the bar;
'y' = bar 1 LH note 2, as it is a single note and the second left-hand event in the bar; and
'z' = bar 1 LH chord 3, as it is a chord (i.e. two or more notes) and the third left-hand event in the bar.

Acknowledgements

Financial support for *The Complete Chopin* has been generously provided by the Arts and Humanities Research Council, the British Academy, the British Council, the Swiss National Science Foundation, and the Department of Music, Royal Holloway, University of London.

John Rink
Jim Samson
Jean-Jacques Eigeldinger
Christophe Grabowski

CRITICAL COMMENTARY*

Op. 10 poses particular editorial challenges, with a very poorly engraved French first edition that nonetheless shows important revisions made at proof stage. Its endemic corruptions were largely carried over to the German and English first editions, both engraved from French proofs; these involve time signatures, accents, dynamics, staccato signs, voicing stems and fingering, often misrendered, inaccurately placed or just omitted. In that context Chopin's proof revisions sometimes suggest makeshift repair, leaving the extant *Stichvorlage* (engraving text) and the French first edition with some variant content that appears equally valid in either source, and often mutually informative. Chopin proofread only the French edition. In the English edition the input of Chopin's assistant Julian Fontana (who was resident in London in 1833) includes added fingering, though Op. 10 No. 1 in particular shows some astute corrective detail, its provenance now impossible to ascertain.

These manifold circumstances prompt close scrutiny of the surviving corpus of primary source material for Op. 10 Nos. 2, 3, 5–7 and 9, specifically to evaluate and, where possible, remedy manifest inaccuracies in the French first edition by reference to its surviving *Stichvorlage* material. Within that corpus, the French first edition remains the principal source for those etudes, interventions from the *Stichvorlage* being limited to correcting obvious omissions or corruptions by the engraver in places where the first edition shows no subsequent revision. (Any debatable cases, such as ties or other indications that Chopin might conceivably have removed at proof stage, are presented in round brackets, as variants.) A few etudes in Op. 10 also show suspect pedalling in the first edition. Probably through the engraver's negligence, the first editions of Op. 10 consistently print **𝄴** where all manuscript sources indicate 𝄵. We might thus infer that the lost *Stichvorlagen* [**A**^{2}] of Etudes 1, 2 and 4 probably indicated 𝄵, like the surviving manuscript sources of these pieces.

Annotations on exemplars belonging to Chopin's sister Ludwika Jędrzejewicz and his pupils Camille Dubois and Jane Stirling are generally assumed to reflect Chopin's intentions. Of the more copious annotations on the exemplars of his pupil Zofia Zaleska-Rosengardt, those of special interest are noted below, along with sparse annotations on the exemplar of Chopin's pupil Napoléon Orda. Later editions by Chopin's pupils Thomas Tellefsen (1860) and Carl Mikuli (1879) are noted, with due circumspection, when they provide relevant variants: both had access to scores annotated by Chopin (at least four different sets in Mikuli's case, all now unlocated) but do not identify sources of individual readings.

Sources

Most sources are viewable online, via www.chopinonline.ac.uk/ocve, www.polona.pl or www.themorgan.org.

C^{Lin} Manuscript copy of early versions of Nos. 1 and 2, attributed to Józef Linowski, devoid of performing indications; No. 2 dated 2 November 1830 [PL-Wmfc, M/190–191]

A^{1} Non-*Stichvorlage* pre-publication autographs of No. 2 – presentation autograph in small format notebook, signed 'Fréd. Chopin' [S-Smf: MMS 398]; No. 3 – early draft, dated (in Polish) 'Paris, 25 August [18]32.' [US-NYpm: C549.E85, Lehman deposit]; No. 4 – early draft, dated (in Polish) 'Paris. August 6, 1832.' [PL-Wmfc: M/3249]; No. 9 – early draft, annotated (in Polish) 'Paris' [US-NYpm: C549.E85, Lehman deposit]

A^{2} Autograph *Stichvorlagen* for **F**^{1} of Nos. 3, 5, 6, 8, 9, 10 [PL-Wmfc: M/192–197]; No. 7 [US-NYpm: C549.E85]; Nos. 11, 12 [S-Smf: MMS 399]

[**A**^{2}] Lost: hypothetical autograph *Stichvorlagen* for **F**^{1} of Nos. 1, 2, 4

F^{0} Early proof for **F**^{1} of No. 2, corrected by Chopin [F-Po: Rés. 50 (4)]

F^{1} French first edition, June 1833. Maurice Schlesinger, Paris, plate no. M. S. 1399 (dedicatee misprinted as 'J. Liszt').

F^{2} Corrected reprint of **F**^{1}, mid-1830s

F^{3} Reprint of **F**^{2}, December 1842. Henry Lemoine, Paris, plate no. 2775. H.L.

F = **F**$^{1-3}$

G^{1} German first edition, August 1833. F. Kistner, Leipzig, 2 vols: Nos. 1–6, plate no. 1018; Nos. 7–12, plate no. 1019 (dedicatee misprinted in vol. 1 as in **F**^{1}).

G^{2} Corrected reprint of **G**^{1}, 1833–40 (corrections to Nos. 2, 3, 4 and dedicatee)

G^{3} German second edition, post-1840, re-engraved with minor emendations. F. Kistner, Leipzig, 2 vols: Nos. 1–6, plate no. 1018; Nos. 7–12, plate no. 1019.

G = **G**$^{1-3}$

[**E1**] Unlocated English first edition, August 1833. Wessel & Co., London, 2 vols: Nos. 1–6, plate no. W. & C° 960; Nos. 7–12, plate no. W. & C° 961.

E^{2} Corrected reprint (?) of **E**^{1}, 1835–36. Dedicated to J. [*sic*] Liszt and F. Hiller, subheaded 'New & Revised Edition ... Edited with additional fingering by his pupil, / I. [*recte* J.] Fontana'.

E^{3} Corrected reprint of **E**^{2} vol. 1, c. 1836–39

E = **E**^{2,3}

D Dubois exemplar of **F**^{3} [F-Pn musique: Rés. F. 980 (I, 1)]

J Jędrzejewicz exemplar of **F**^{3} [PL-Wmfc: M/174]

O Orda exemplar of **F**^{2} [PL-Wmfc: M/610]

S Stirling exemplar of **F**^{2} [F-Pn musique: Rés. Vma 241 (I, 10)]

ZR Zaleska-Rosengardt exemplar of **F**^{2} [F-Ppo: FN 15818 (a)]

Tel Tellefsen edition (Op. 10 and Op. 25 only). Richault, Paris, 1860.

Mik Mikuli edition (all 27 etudes). Kistner, Leipzig, 1879 (republished by Schirmer, New York, 1895, in a different engraving that sometimes reads differently).

G and **E**, as offshoots of **F**^{1} unmediated by Chopin, are mentioned below only when they vary significantly from **F**. Apart from a few designated musical variants, details from **G** and **E** are introduced (in round brackets) only when they match or complete the sense of extant indications; any that affect pitch or rhythm are treated as editorial interventions.

Suggested filiation

Surviving autograph *Stichvorlagen* of Etudes 3 and 5–12 served for **F**^{1}, late proofs for which (now lost) served for engraving **G**^{1} and **E**^{1}. An exemplar of **F**^{1} revised by Chopin would have served for **F**^{2}, though some irregularities suggest mishaps or peripheral input.

No. 1 in C major

Principal source: **F**^{2}

Early source filiation. **C**^{Lin} is an early version, presumably copied from an early autograph now lost. Besides some obvious copying errors, its most notable variants are RH e^{1}, not d^{1}, at beat 4 of bars 4 and 52; e^{2}, not $e\flat^{2}$, at bar 60 beat 3; and c^{1}, not b, at bar 64 beat 4 (each leaving exposed parallel fifths that **F** remedies).

Bass notation and ties. **C**^{Lin} notates LH mostly in shorthand as upper note with *8* underneath (in this Etude clearly signifying *coll'8*^{a}); **F** does likewise where space is cramped, otherwise spelling out LH octaves. In the process **F** omits the upper tie in bars 7–8, 9–10, 11–12, 13–14, 73–74 and 75–76 (evident oversights); here by analogy with bars 1–2, 15–16 (as implicit in **C**^{Lin}, and as in **G**, **E** bars 7–14, **G** bars 73–76). **F**: LH notation in bars 49–50, 65–66 respectively [music example], [music example],

* The editor of this volume has produced a more extensive Critical Commentary which can be found at www.fabermusic.com.

notated here with lower octave in bars 49, 65 (as in $\mathbf{E}^{3}$ bar 65); LH notation in bars 57–58 , read here as tied octaves, though the intent may have been (see bars 33–34, 69–70 and comment below concerning dynamics; the equivalent at bars 57–58 might have been overlooked if [$\mathbf{A}^{2}$] indicated bars 51–59 as reprising bars 3–11).

Dynamics. Comparison between **F** and the surviving *Stichvorlagen* of Op. 10 suggests that the engraving manuscript of this etude, now lost, may have shown more dynamics than **F** does, with a drop in dynamics implicit before bar 33. As Chopin indicates no dynamic level between ***p*** and ***f*** in Op. 10, ***p*** may be assumed as implied at bars 37, 49 and 77. (Note the single bass note in the implicitly quieter bars 33, 37, 39, 41, 67, 69 and 71.)

Pedalling. Atypically for Chopin, the pedalling in **F** often blurs harmonic motion or stepwise motion in melody or bass (e.g. bars 5, 8, 18, 26, 51–52). Editorial intervention is restricted to obvious cases, though Chopin's norms might also suggest discretionary pedal within bars 8, 38, 40 or 56.

Bars 5, 53. **F**: last RH note a^3, not b^3 (the passage possibly notated only once in [**A2**]), probably a misprint; here as $\mathbf{C}^{\mathrm{Lin}}$ (also **E**), supported by a line in **S** at bar 5 under the notehead suggestive of correction to b^3

Bars 5–6. LH slur by analogy with bars 53–54

Bar 27. **F**: pianistically implausible fingering '3', not '4', to RH note 3; here by analogy with RH note 7 (**E** as here)

Bar 29. **F**: last RH note c^4, not $b\flat^3$ as per prevailing pattern; probably a misprint, given that bar 30 RH note 2 would then need fingering *3*, not *4*; here as $\mathbf{C}^{\mathrm{Lin}}$ (also **E**)

Bars 36–37. **D**: slur-like arc pencilled by Chopin, beginning above bar 36, ending bar 37 LH note 1, then a rising arc from there, suggesting structural articulation at beginning of bar 37 (hence broken line here defining extent of *dim.*)

Bar 43. **F**: first ✻ aligned under RH note 6 (squashed into available space); here as in bars 42, 44 (also **G**)

Bar 44. **F**: second *Ped.* aligned under RH note 11 (restricted space under preceding bass octave); here as in bar 43 (also $\mathbf{G}^{3}$)

Bars 45, 46. RH 𝄽 at beat 4 from $\mathbf{C}^{\mathrm{Lin}}$, **G**

Bar 46. ✻ from **E**

Bar 48. **F**: ✻ appears under RH note 8 between staves, squashed between *dim.* and >, with no space later in bar; here by analogy with harmony

Bar 57–58. See comments above concerning bass notation and ties

Bar 60. **F**: long accent appears under RH note 13, probably oversight from earlier version where ♭ was introduced only at RH note 13 (as in $\mathbf{C}^{\mathrm{Lin}}$); relocated here by analogy with voice motion over changing octaves in bars 8, 38, 40, 56

Bar 62. Fingering to RH note 5 from **G**, **E**

Bar 63. **F**: fingering '1' to RH note 4, not RH note 5; here as in beat 1

Bar 71. Precautionary ♮ to RH note 2 from $\mathbf{G}^{3}$

Bar 77. Fingering from **S**

No. 2 in A minor

Principal source: $\mathbf{F}^{2}$. **F** shows revisions made at a late proof stage subsequent to $\mathbf{F}^{0}$; reference is made to Chopin's annotations in $\mathbf{F}^{0}$ to identify engraving inaccuracies or oversights in **F**.

Source relationships. $\mathbf{C}^{\mathrm{Lin}}$, the earliest source, has LH $f\sharp$ (not f) at beat 2 of bars 4, 12 and 39, and no flats to b or b^1 in bars 17 and 44. Unlike the later $\mathbf{A}^{1}$, $\mathbf{C}^{\mathrm{Lin}}$ matches the RH lower-voice semiquaver durations of **F**. $\mathbf{F}^{0}$ is probably a first proof, its only printed performing indications comprising six dynamic markings (one deleted by Chopin, three others suspect) plus fingering at bar 35. Its printed LH durations match those in $\mathbf{C}^{\mathrm{Lin}}$, with various crotchet stems amended by Chopin to quavers and/or staccato dots added. Otherwise Chopin's annotations correct misprints and supply the remaining fingering plus most performing indications. **F** shows further additions and retouches evidently made on later proofs. $\mathbf{A}^{1}$, external to the publication chain, appears to date from around the proofing stage for $\mathbf{F}^{1}$. The sole source of several essential accidentals, it shares readings variously with $\mathbf{C}^{\mathrm{Lin}}$ and $\mathbf{F}^{0}$ (notably Chopin's annotations in $\mathbf{F}^{0}$). Its variants, consistent across parallel passages, notably involve RH lower-voice durations, with bars 3–4, 11–12 and 38–39 appearing thus for RH:

(lower-voice durations likewise in bars 16–18, 43–44 and second half of bars 45 and 46), bars 19–20 thus:

(and analogously until middle of bar 24), bar 27 RH thus:

,

bar 28 analogously, bars 32–35 RH thus:

and bar 48 RH thus:

Bar 1. $\mathbf{A}^{1}$: tempo indication *Vivace* 𝅗𝅥 = 69

Bar 4. $\mathbf{F}^{0}$, **F**: < spanning beat 4 (probable misprint; $\mathbf{A}^{1}$: > or long accent, ending RH note 15; see also bar 12). **F**: upper fingering appears erroneously to RH notes 1–3, not RH notes 2–4; here as annotated by Chopin in $\mathbf{F}^{0}$. Tie to bs LH chords 2–3 from $\mathbf{A}^{1}$ (also **G**).

Bars 4, 12. $\mathbf{F}^{0}$ variant: lower-voice semiquaver flags printed in $\mathbf{F}^{0}$ deleted by Chopin

Bar 6. **F**: no staccato dot to LH chord 1 (cf. bars 2, 14, 37, 41); here as per Chopin's annotation in $\mathbf{F}^{0}$

Bar 7. $\mathbf{C}^{\mathrm{Lin}}$, $\mathbf{F}^{0}$, **G**: no ♮ to g^2 RH chord 5; **G** analogously adds ♯ to g^1 LH chord 2

Bar 8. **F**: > between staves under RH notes 2–4 (inaccurate rendering of Chopin's annotation on $\mathbf{F}^{0}$: long accent above LH chord 2, ***fz*** not present, evidently added remedially on a later proof). Precautionary ♮ to RH note 2 from **G**.

Bar 12. $\mathbf{F}^{0}$, **F**: ***f*** under LH chord 2, possibly corruption of intended ***fz*** (cf. bar 8) or of a clarifying 'f' or 'fa' written by the note f on [$\mathbf{A}^{2}$] (as annotated by Chopin in bars 7, 25 in $\mathbf{F}^{0}$). > to RH notes 14–16 from $\mathbf{A}^{1}$ (see comment to bar 4).

Bars 12, 39. Tie to bs LH chords 2–3 as in bar 4 (also present in **G**)

Bar 13. **F**^{0}, **F**: *sempre legato* appears instead in bar 11 (as annotated by Chopin in **F**^{0}), also in bar 21, doubtless as reminders beginning new pages; here by analogy with bars 1, 5. **F**: no ♮ to a^1 RH chord 5, d^2 RH chord 9 (cf. bars 1, 9; **A**^{1} as here).

Bars 16, 47. ***f*** from **A**^{1} (defining extent of *crescendo*)

Bar 17. **F**: no staccato dot to LH note 1, no slur to LH chords 2–3, no staccato dot to LH chord 3; oversights of Chopin's annotations in **F**^{0} (squashed into cramped space between systems)

Bars 17, 44. **F**: final LH > (not present in **C**^{Lin}, **F**^{0}) appears to RH, not LH (here by analogy with bar 30; **A**^{1} as here in bar 44)

Bar 18. Staccato dots to LH chords 2, 3 as per Chopin's annotations in **F**^{0} (**G**: slur instead to LH chords 2–3)

Bars 18–19. **F**^{0}: RH slur initially added by Chopin above the notes, extending beyond bar 18 (where system breaks), then overwritten with fingering, the slur renotated under the notes, not continued in bar 19 on new system; *sempre legato* in bar 19 (added by Chopin above the new system brace) might thus be read as *de facto* continuation of the slur as written in **F**^{0} (see bar 35, but also **A**^{1}, where RH phrasing breaks over this barline, with long accent to bar 19 RH chord 1)

Bars 19–20, 21–23. **F**: *poco a poco cresc.* appears twice, in bars 19–20 preceding page turn, then as here in bars 21–23 (neither indication present in **F**^{0}), probably erroneous duplication; here by analogy with rising sequence from bar 21 (see analogous variant Etude 5 bars 24–25)

Bar 20. **F**: no fingering to lower note RH chord 1 (cf. bar 21; here as per Chopin's annotation in **F**^{0})

Bar 23. **F**^{0}, **F**: LH chord 4 contains e^1, probably misprint for c^1 (as added by Chopin in **F**^{0}, leaving e^1 undeleted possibly by oversight); here by analogy with bar 21, also as **C**^{Lin}, **A**^{1} (note the absence otherwise of four-note chords in bars 19–24)

Bar 24. ♮ to middle note RH chord 13 implicit in **C**^{Lin}, **A**^{1}, where beat 4 is notated an octave lower with *8*- - - above

Bar 25. **F**: no fingering to lower note RH chord 1 (cf. equivalent in bar 26; here as per Chopin's annotation in **F**^{0})

Bars 25, 26. Alternative fingering '*4*' to bar 25 RH note 16, bar 26 RH chord 1 as per Chopin's annotations in **F**^{0}

Bar 26. ⟩ to beat 4 by analogy with bar 25

Bar 27. **F**: Staccato dot to LH chord 1 from **A**^{1}, **F**^{0} (Chopin's annotation)

Bar 28. Staccato dot to LH chord 1 from **A**^{1}

Bar 30. > to LH chord 4 from **E**, **G**^{3}; staccato dot to LH chord 3 by analogy with bar 31

Bar 31. RH variant: the tied-over a^1 presupposes fingering *3* to RH note 4 (no fingering in **A**^{1}); the same repeated a^1 appears in **C**^{Lin}, **F**^{0} but without a tie. Upper slur to LH chords 2–3 from **A**^{1}; staccato dot to LH chord 3 as per Chopin's annotation in **F**^{0}.

Bar 37. Lower note LH chord 1 from **C**^{Lin} (consistent with a corresponding addition by Chopin in **F**^{0} at bar 14; see also bars 2, 6, 10, 41)

Bar 38. **F**^{0}, **F**: top note RH chord 9 spelled $e\flat^2$; here as in bars 3, 11, also **C**^{Lin}, **A**^{1}

Bar 41. **F**^{0}, **F**: RH note 7 spelled $e\flat^3$; here as in bars 2, 6, 10, 14, 37, also **C**^{Lin}, **A**^{1} (though cf. bars 16, 43)

Bar 44. **F**^{0}: no printed ♭ or ♮ to b/b^1 in this bar (consistent with **C**^{Lin}); annotated by Chopin as **F**^{0} variant and LH here

No. 3 in E major

Principal source: **F**^{2}. **F** shows significant revisions made at proof stage; reference is made to **A**^{2}, as *Stichvorlage*, to identify engraving inaccuracies or oversights.

Suggested filiation. **A**^{1}, headed 'Etude', probably served as preparatory draft for **A**^{2}; it indicates bars 62–72 just by 'da capo al segno ⊕' after bar 61, with ⊕ marked at the end of bar 19 (the final version's elision between bars 1 and 9 not specified). Bars 30–31 and 34–35 appear there essentially as here, using 𝄎 as shorthand symbol for each hand in bar 31 and RH in bar 36, the RH modal alterations then sketched in around these.

A = **A**^{1,2}

Bar 0. **A**^{1}: tempo indication *Vivace*. **A**^{2}: tie-like curve from below RH *b*, ending left of ***p*** before barline, possibly readable as an open tenuto tie implying finger overlap with ensuing e^1.

Bars 1–3, 8–9, 62. **A**^{2}: lines curving under lower staff upper-voice semiquavers through bars 1–2, bar 8 beat 2 and bar 62 beat 1 delineate RH from LH (not readable as slurs)

Bars 6, 8. RH fingering from **D** (final '*1*' in bar 8 faint)

Bars 7, 8, 23, 25, 27, 29. RH arpeggiation signs in bars 7, 8, 23 from **D**, indicating note order as [music example] (and equivalently); similar arpeggiation may be assumed around remaining RH grace notes in bars 23, 25, 27, 29

Bars 8, 13. **F**: no crotchet upstem to LH note 4 (cf. LH note 1 and surrounding bars; **A**^{2} as here)

Bars 14, 15. **A**^{2}: > to RH chord 3, apparently removed at proof stage for **F**^{1} (traces reappear in **F**^{2,3} in bar 14)

Bar 15. LH > by analogy with bar 14

Bar 17. **F**: no *ten.* to LH chord 1 (cf. RH), no slur to RH chords 5–8 (cf. RH and bars 72, 73 respectively; **A**^{2} as here)

Bar 18. **F**: no ⟩ (cf. bar 17; **A**^{2} as here)

Bars 18–20. **F**: no LH sustaining crotchet or quaver stems (**A**^{2} as here, except **A** has crotchet not quaver stem bar 20 beat 2)

Bar 19. **F**: no RH long accent (cf. bar 72; **A**^{2} as here)

Bar 21. **F**: *poco più animato* (not present in **A**) begins above first RH grace note (indication forced left by page break after bar 21); here in accordance with phrasing and texture. Beat 1 RH/LH liaison from **D**, indicating simultaneous attack on the beat.

Bar 29. **F**: additional staccato dots to LH notes 6, 7 (apparent engraver error, hence removal here, as per **A**^{2})

Bar 34. **A**, **F**^{1}: no ♮ to lower note RH chord 2; **F**^{2,3}: RH chord 2 as here, then ♮, not ♯, to upper note RH chord 3 (implausibly leaving no distinction from bar 35: cf. bar 30); RH chord 3 here as in **A**, **F**^{1} (**G** instead has no ♮ to RH chords 1, 2). **F**: no > to RH chord 3 (cf. bar 30; **A**^{2} as here). > to RH chord 6 from **E**.

Bar 35. > to RH chords 3, 6 from **A**^{1}

Bar 36. Precautionary ♯ to upper note RH chord 1 from **A**^{1}, to lower note RH chord 1 from **G**^{3}

Bar 38. Precautionary ♮ to lower note RH chord 1 from **G**^{3}; staccato dot to LH chord 1 from **G**

Bar 39. Fingering to RH chords 2–8 from **S**

Bar 40. Staccato dot to RH/LH chord 1 from **G**

Bar 41. Fingering from **S** (where '*4*' also appears above LH chord 4, probably error for '*1*'); ♮ to lower note LH chord 8 from **D** (maintaining tritones in each hand throughout bars 38–41; **G**: ♯ instead)

Bars 41–45. Slurs from **E**^{3} bar 41 RH chord 4 to bar 42 RH chord 1, bar 42 LH chord 4 to bar 43 LH chord 1, bar 44 LH chord 4 to bar 45 LH chord 1

Bar 42. **F**: no slur to RH chords 4–5 (**A**^{2} as here). **A**^{2}: first vertical stroke of ***ff*** thin and faint, second stroke close against it, heavily emphasised, possibly ***f*** intended (cf. bar 46). Fingering from **S** (final '*3*' unclear).

Bars 42, 43, 45, 46, 48, 50, 54. **F**: no 𝆮 indications (cf. bar 44; **A**^{2} as here)

Bar 43. **F**: no ✻ (cf. bar 45; **A**^{2} as here)

Bars 44–45. **F**: no *sempre più*, no < (**A²** as here)
Bar 47. Fingering from **D**
Bar 52. **F**: no slur to LH chords 2–3 (**A²** as here). Slur to LH chords 4–5 from **G**, **E**.
Bar 54. **F**: ***f***, not ***fz*** (cf. preceding dynamics; **A²** as here); no > to RH chord 6 (cf. bar 55; **A²** as here)
Bar 55. **F**: no staccato dot to LH note 1 (cf. ensuing bars; **A²** as here)
Bars 55–56. **F**: no RH tie over barline (cf. bars 54–55; **A** as here); ensuing slur begins bar 56 RH note 1, not RH note 2 (cf. bar 54; **A²** as here). LH slur over barline as in bars 54–55.
Bars 55, 57, 58, 59. **F**: ▾, not staccato dot, to LH note 5 (**A²** as here)
Bar 56. **F**: no staccato dots to LH (cf. surrounding bars; **A²** as here)
Bars 56, 58. **A²**: > to last lower staff quaver appears under *g*♮ quaver beam, immediately to right of *B* notehead, ambiguously readable to either LH *B* or RH *g*♮ (or both; **F** as here; see comment to bar 57)
Bar 57. **F**: no RH slur, long accent erroneously above upper staff note 2, not note 3 (**A²** as here); lower staff > appears under final LH *B* (apparent misrendering of **A²**: > written through *g*♮ quaver downstem, as also in bar 59 beat 1, clearly intended for *g*♮)
Bars 58, 59. **F**: no > to beat 1 *g*♮, no downstem or connecting quaver beam to same note and ensuing *f*[♯] (cf. surrounding beats; **A²** as here)
Bar 59. **F**: no LH 𝄾 at end of bar (**A²** as here)
Bar 60. **F**: no upstem between initial *f*[♯] and *e¹* (**A²** as here)
Bar 61. ***pp*** from **D**
Bar 63. **F**: no RH slurs (cf. bars 64, 66–67; **A²** as here). Long accent to RH chord 3 from **A²**.
Bar 64. Long accent to RH chord 5 from **A²**; RH slur beat 2 from **G²˒³**, **E³**
Bar 65. **F**: lower note RH chord 1 *a*, not *b* (cf. bar 4; here as amended by hand in **S**, **J**, as per **A**); no > (**A²** as here)
Bars 65–66. **F**: no lower staff slur over barline (cf. bars 12–13; **A²** as here). RH tie over barline from **A¹** (these bars indicated as reprise of bars 4–5).
Bar 67. Beat 2 RH slur from **E³**
Bars 67, 68. **A²**, **F**: > to RH chord 3, probably unintended remnants (see comment to bars 14, 15), hence removal here
Bar 68. **F**: no RH slur beat 2 (cf. bar 15; **A²** as here). Beat 1 RH slurs from **G³**, **E³**.
Bar 70. **A²**, **F**: additional > above RH chords 5–8 (probably slip of the pen for slur, as per bar 17, hence slur here)
Bars 71, 73–76. **F**: no LH crotchet upstems (cf. bars 1–15, 18–20; **A²** as here)
Bar 74. **F**: lower staff upper note 5 *b*, not *a* (cf. bar 73; here as amended by hand in **S**, as per **A**)
Bars 76–77. *attacca il presto con fuoco* from **A²** (written after final barline)

No. 4 in C♯ minor

Principal source: **F**

Suggested filiation. **A¹** probably served as preparatory draft for [**A²**], forming a pair with **A¹** of No. 3, though No. 4 is in a more finished state. Besides the variants shown, its main textural differences from **F** are that bars 5 and 55 have no *b¹* in RH chord 1 (imitating four bars earlier), bar 50 has a bar's rest for LH (followed by 𝒫𝑒𝒹. and ***fz*** at bar 51 LH note 1), and bar 81 doubles LH note 1 at the lower octave. Articulation and dynamics in **A¹** are often close enough to **F** to throw light on probable engraving corruptions in the latter.

Bars 0–1. **D**: RH vertical stroke signifying articulation break after bar 1 RH note 1. Initial RH/LH slur from **A¹**.
Bar 1. **F**: ***fp*** at RH/LH chord 1, not a normal indication in Chopin's piano music, probably corruption of ***fzp*** (as here by analogy with **A¹**: ***fz***, no ensuing *cresc.*)
Bars 1–2. Fingering from **S**
Bar 3. Arpeggiation sign to LH chord 2 from **G**
Bar 4. Staccato dot to LH chord 1 from **G**; crotchet downstem to LH chord 7 from **A¹**
Bars 4–6. **F**: LH slur in bar 6 only (to LH notes 1–16), beginning new system; probably corruption (**A¹**: LH slur beginning bar 4 beat 4 tails off near end of bar 5); here by analogy with phrasing continuity over bars 1–2 RH
Bar 5. ***p***, *cresc.* by analogy with bar 1
Bar 7. LH slurs, > to RH chord 2 from **A¹** (see bars 3, 57)
Bar 8. **F**: ***fp*** at RH/LH chord 1 (probably corruption of ***fzp***: see comment to bar 1); RH downstems and quaver beams (not present in **A¹**) link RH notes 2, 4, 6, then RH notes 8, 10, 12, 14 (doubtless corruption; here as in LH)
Bar 10. Fingering to RH note 5 from **D**, **S**; other fingering from **D**
Bar 11. ***f*** from **A¹**; RH slurs from **E³** (see bar 3); first LH arpeggiation sign from **G²˒³**, **E³**, others from **G²˒³**; > to LH chord 4 from **E³**
Bar 12. **F**: ***f*** to LH chord 7 (implausible, presumably corruption of ***fz***). ***ff*** from **A¹** (see bar 62)
Bar 13. Fingering from **A¹**
Bar 15. **F**: LH note 3 *A*♯ (clashing implausibly with RH *a¹*); in **A¹** it appears as *B*♮ (see bars 65, 66); analogy with bars 13, 14 suggests it was respelled as *A*𝄪 on [**A²**] or proofs (see also bars 63, 64), the 𝄪 sign incompletely printed in **F** (which uses ♯̤ to denote 𝄪 throughout Op. 10). Long accent to RH chord 4 from **A¹**.
Bar 16. **F**: ***f*** at RH chord 4 (presumably corruption of ***fz*** as in bars 18, 20, 22)
Bars 16–17. **A¹**, **F**: LH slur ends bar 16 LH note 16; here as amended by hand in **S** (see RH). RH slur over barline from **D**.
Bars 19–20. **F**: LH slur ends bar 19 LH note 16, new slur bar 20 LH notes 1–4 (probably corruption: cf. bars 17–18 RH, which bars 19–20 answer in imitation); here by analogy with bars 9–10, 17–18
Bar 20. Fingering from **S**
Bars 20, 22. > from **A¹**
Bar 21. Fingering from **D**
Bars 21–22. **F**: RH slur ends at barline after bar 21, new slur from bar 22 RH note 1 (on same system), possibly confusion from a system break in [**A²**]; here by analogy with bars 9–10, 17–18
Bar 22. LH staccato dots from **E³** (see bar 18)
Bar 23. RH staccato dots from **G²˒³** (see bar 19)
Bars 23–24. **F**: LH slur (not present in **A¹**) ends bar 23 LH note 16 at end of system, new system from bar 24 begins with carried-over RH slur; here by analogy with bars 1–2, 15–16, 27–28, 66–67 (**G** as here)
Bar 25. **F**: fingering '2' to upper note RH chord 1 (doubtless misprint for '3'); here by analogy with bars 26, 27. Staccato dot to LH chord 3 from **G**.
Bar 26. **F**: fingering '3' to upper note RH chord 1 (already in effect from bar 25 RH note 16, hence removal here); staccato dot, not ▾, to RH chord 13 (here by analogy with bar 25); ***f***, not ***fz***, at beat 4 (cf. surrounding dynamics; **A¹**: ***fz***). RH slur by analogy with bar 25; precautionary ♮ to RH note 14 from **A¹**.
Bar 27. Fingering from **D**
Bar 28. **A¹**, **F**: no cancelling ♮ to upper note LH chord 3 (see LH chord 4)
Bar 29. **F**: no ♯ to RH note 15 (cf. RH note 3, also bar 30; **A¹** as here). Fingering from **D**.
Bars 29–30. **F**: RH slur (not present in **A¹**) ends bar 29 RH note 16 at end of system, new system from bar 30 begins with carried-over RH slur; here by analogy with bars 27–28, 31–32
Bar 30. Slur to LH notes 2–5 from **E³**, **G³**
Bar 34. **F**: ***fp***, not ***fz***, to RH chord 3 (doubtless corruption: cf. ensuing ***f***)
Bar 35. Fingering from **S**; ▾ to LH note 1 from **G**, **E³**
Bars 35, 36. LH slurs bar 35 from **E³**, bar 36 by analogy
Bar 38. < from **A¹**

Bars 38–39. Slur beginning bar 38 RH chord 3 from **G**
Bar 39. ▾ to RH/LH beat 1 from **G**, **E**^{3}
Bar 41. < from **A**^{1}; second RH slur from **G**^{3}, **E**^{3}; third RH slur from **E**^{3}
Bar 42. **F**: long accent under RH notes 7–8, then > under RH notes 9–11 (doubtless corruption; here by analogy with bar 43 and as in **A**^{1}). Precautionary 𝄪 to LH note 14 from **G**^{3}.
Bars 42, 43. **A**^{1}, **F**: no ♯ to LH note 15; here by analogy with beat 3 and RH. Bar 42 RH slurs, bar 43 first RH slur from **E**.
Bars 42–44. LH slurs from **E** in bars 42–43, from **E**^{3} in bar 44
Bar 45. Fingering from **S**
Bars 45–46. **F**: *con forza* from bar 46 RH/LH note 1, probably to mark LH entry at bar 45 beat 4 but forced into bar 46 by system break after bar 45 (compare **A**^{1}, in which ***ff*** appears under bar 45 RH note 10, where LH originally entered an octave below RH; LH later amended as here, leaving ***ff*** unamended but clearly intended for LH entry; *con forza* here by analogy). Slur beginning bar 45 LH note 3 from **E**^{3}.
Bar 47. Fingering to RH note 2 from **S**, to RH notes 4, 6 from **A**^{1}; LH ▾ from **A**^{1}
Bars 47, 48. **A**^{1}, **F**: no ♮ to RH note 15; here by analogy with bar 47 RH note 3
Bars 47–52. **F**: RH slur extends beyond bar 47, where page ends, contradicted by new slur bar 48 RH notes 1–16; new slur beginning bar 49 RH note 1 extends beyond bar 49, where system ends, contradicted by new slur from bar 50 RH note 1; here by sequential logic (avoiding phrase breaks in middle of chromatic sequence)
Bars 48, 49. LH arpeggiation sign from **A**^{1} (where it appears in bar 48, with 𝄎 used as shorthand for bar 49 LH)
Bar 49. > to RH note 1 from **A**^{1} (where it appears in bar 48, with 𝄎 used as shorthand for bar 49 RH notes 1–12)
Bar 53. LH staccato dots, first arpeggiation sign from **G**, **E**^{3}; second arpeggiation sign from **G**
Bar 54. ▾ to RH/LH chord 1 from **G**, **E**^{3}; > to last RH chord from **A**^{1}; crotchet downstem to LH chord 7 by analogy with bar 4, also bar 53 LH chord 4
Bars 54–56. **F**: LH slur beginning bar 54 extends beyond bar 55 LH note 16, where system ends, contradicted by new slur from bar 56 LH note 1; here by analogy with bars 51–52 RH (which bars 55–56 answer in imitation)
Bar 55. **F**: ***f***, not ***fz*** (redundant after bar 54 ***f***); here by analogy with bar 1
Bar 58. **F**: RH downstems and quaver beams (not present in **A**^{1}) link RH chord 1 with RH notes 2, 4, then RH notes 6, 8, 10, 12, 14 (here as in LH). RH >s, < from **A**^{1}.
Bars 59–60. **F**: RH slur ends bar 59 RH note 16, new slur bar 60 RH notes 1–4 (**A**^{1}: RH slur from bar 59 RH note 1 extends beyond bar 59 at end of system, without subsequent continuation on new system); here by analogy with bars 9–10, 17–18, 51–52
Bar 60. Fingering from **D**
Bar 61. RH slurs from **E**^{3}; LH staccato dots, first arpeggiation sign from **G**, **E**^{3}; other arpeggiation signs from **G**
Bar 63. LH slur from **A**^{1}
Bars 63, 64. **F**: > after RH chord 1 (not present in **A**^{1}), aligned above LH notes 2–4 (contradicting <; probably inaccurate rendering of a long accent in [**A**^{2}]); here by analogy with similar engraving inaccuracies in Etudes 2, 6
Bars 66–67. RH ties over barline by analogy with bars 15–16, also implied by upbeat accent and RH slur
Bars 68–69. **F**: no LH slur bar 68; LH slur then begins implausibly bar 69 LH note 5 (here by analogy with RH); musical sense suggests that in bar 68 RH/LH phrasing was possibly meant to continue unbroken from bar 67

Bar 75. LH slurs from **G**, **E**^{3}
Bar 76–78. Slur to bar 77 LH notes 1–4 from **G**, other LH slurs from **G**^{3}
Bar 78. Precautionary ♮ to RH/LH note 1 from **A**^{1}
Bar 79. **F**: Ped. appears under RH note 3, ***ff*** under bar 79 RH notes 8–9 (readable as applying throughout the bar, as here)
Bars 79–80. **F**: slur bar 79 RH notes 2–11, then another slur bar 80 RH notes 6–16 (space in between obstructed by *ottava* line and ensuing 'Loco'); RH slur here by analogy with bars 45–46

No. 5 in G♭ major

Principal source: **F**^{2}. **F** shows significant revisions made at proof stage; reference is made to **A**^{2} and **D** to address engraving or proofing inaccuracies or oversights.

Dynamics, articulation, pedalling. Chopin revised this etude thoroughly at proof stage. **A**^{2} shows a dynamically lighter concept (see footnote variant bars 1–3, whose texture recurs in bars 5–6, 9–11, 13–14, 49–51, 53–54), with no opening tempo or metronome indication, LH staccato only as shown in the present footnote variant in bar 2 and its reprises plus bar 3, pedalling marked only in bars 33–40 and 63–66, and dynamics marked only in bars 7–8, 24–33, 45–46 and 63 onwards, with a dynamically inverted dénouement (see comment to bars 62–65). The pedalling added in **F** raises various queries of placing, blurring and missing releases; the relevance of pedalling in bars 5 and 13 might also be queried (cf. bars 1, 9, 49, 53).

Bar 2. **F**: no fingering to RH note 2 (cf. bar 5: **A**^{2} as here)
Bars 2, 14, 50. **F**: * appears at LH chord 3, not LH chord 2 (blurring harmonies; here as in bar 6)
Bar 3. **F**: no fingering to RH note 5 (cf. bar 15; **A**^{2} as here); first * appears under LH chord 3, second Ped. sign (implausibly) just before LH note 4 (here as in bar 51). Fingering '*4*' to RH notes 4, 10 from **D**; staccato dot to LH chord 3 from **E**.
Bar 4. **A**^{2}, **F**: RH note 9 *d*[♭]^3 (cf. bars 12, 52; here as amended in **D**, probably by Chopin)
Bars 4, 7. Fingering to RH note 4 from **D**
Bars 4, 12. **F**: * appears under LH chord 2, then additional Ped. * under RH notes 7–12 (contradicting LH articulation and final 𝄾); here as in bar 52
Bar 5. LH staccato dots from **E**^{3} (see bars 1, 9)
Bar 7. Staccato dots, pedalling from **E**^{3} (see bar 15)
Bar 9. Precautionary ♭ to LH chord 1 from **G**
Bars 10, 54. * as in bar 6
Bar 11. Added pedalling as in bar 51
Bar 12. **F**: no LH accent (cf. bar 4; **A**^{2}, **E**^{3} as here)
Bar 13. * from **G** (see bar 5)
Bar 16. **F**: no fingering to RH note 1 (cf. bar 15; **A**^{2} as here). * from **G**^{3}.
Bars 17, 18, 21. **F**: long accent (not present in **A**^{2}) appears against RH, not LH (engraving inaccuracy; here as in bars 69–70, 73–74)
Bars 17, 18, 21, 22. Beat 2 LH slur in bars 17, 18, 21 from **E**^{3}; beat 1 LH slur in bar 18 from **G**^{3}, **E**^{3}; bar 22 LH slurs from **E**^{3}
Bar 18. **F**: RH slur ends RH note 9 (misreading of **A**^{2}: as here)
Bars 18, 22. **F**: no fingering to RH note 10 (cf, bar 17; **A**^{2} as here)
Bars 19–22. **A**^{2}, **F**: RH slur ends bar 19 RH note 12 (further extension obstructed by ensuing *ottava* line); here by analogy with bars 16–18, also implied by *cresc.* in bar 19
Bar 22. LH long accent by analogy with bar 18
Bar 23. [***p***] in relation to preceding *cresc.* and ensuing *poco a poco cresc.*
Bar 24. **A**^{2}, **F**: RH note 7 *e*[♭]^3 (here as amended by hand in **S**). **F**: slur to RH notes 1–6, not RH notes 2–7, possibly the result of confusion with bar 25 (cf. bar 23; **A**^{2} as here). Staccato dot to LH chord 2 from **G**.

Bars 24, 25. **F**: no ▾ to RH note 1 (cf. RH note 7; **A**^{2} as here)

Bars 24–25. **F**: no slur bar 24 RH note 8 to bar 25 RH note 1 (cf. bars 23–24, 25–26; **A**^{2} as here). **E**^{3}: slur bar 24 LH chord 3 to bar 25 LH chord 1.

Bar 25. **F**: fingering '3', not '4', to RH note 2 (possibly confusion with bar 24; **A**^{2} as here). * from **E**.

Bars 25, 26. **F**: Ped. appears after LH chord 1 (no space under chord); here as in bars 27–32. Staccato dot to LH chord 2 from **E**^{3} (see bar 23).

Bars 25–26. **F**: slurs to bar 25 RH notes 1–5 (ending just after RH note 5) and 8–12, then to bar 26 RH notes 1–6, 8–12 (inaccurate renderings of **A**^{2}: as here, except RH slur extends beyond bar 25, where system ends, without subsequent completion on new system; cf. slurs ending RH note 1 in bars 24, 25)

Bar 27. **F**: no fingering to RH note 3 (**A**^{2} as here)

Bars 28–29. **F**: no LH slur over barline (cf. bars 27–28; **A**^{2} as here)

Bar 29. **F**: no staccato dot to LH chord 1 (cf. bar 30; **A**^{2} as here); staccato dot to LH chord 2 by analogy with bar 30

Bar 31. **F**: RH note 5 misprinted as $b[\flat]^2$ (here as corrected by hand in **D**, **S**, **J**, as per **A**^{2}); no fingering to RH notes 5, 6, 9 (cf. bar 32 RH notes 1–2; **A**^{2} as here, also **S** at RH note 6). LH variant from **Mik** is supported by voice-leading and harmonic logic (chromatic rising motion from bar 25, preparing D♭ major arrival at bar 41) and by Chopin's frequent omission elsewhere of cancelling accidentals.

Bars 31–32. RH slur from **A**^{2} (where it begins high above bar 31 RH note 12; cf. bar 16)

Bar 32. **F**: the sudden lurch in voice-leading to $e[\flat]^1$ in LH chord 2, interrupting the surrounding $d[\flat]^1$ pedal point, suggests that $e[\flat]^1$ is either a misprint for $d[\flat]^1$ or was added at proof stage to reinforce the chord (a revision reciprocal to bars 34–35), thus: 

, the $d[\flat]^1$ possibly then having been removed in error. **F**: fingering to RH note 3 misprinted as '1' (here as corrected by hand in **D**, **ZR**, as per **A**^{2}). ***fz*** from **A**^{2}.

Bars 32–33. **F**: no LH slur over barline (**A**^{2} as here)

Bar 33. **F**: no fingering to RH note 1 (cf. bars 34, 35, 37; **A**^{2} as here)

Bars 33–34. **F**: < ends bar 33 RH note 12, without subsequent continuation on next system; here by analogy with bars 37–38

Bars 33–36. **F**: no RH slur bar 33 at end of system, new system from bar 34 begins with carried-over slur (**A**^{2} as here)

Bars 34–35. **F**: ***f*** appears implausibly under bar 34 LH chord 2, possibly corruption of ***fz*** intended to bar 35 LH chord 1 as here

Bar 40. **F**: fingering '5' erroneously appears to RH note 2, not RH note 3 (**A**^{2} as here)

Bar 41. **A**^{2}: fingering '5', not '4', to RH notes 2, 4, 10, 12 (evidently amended as here at proof stage)

Bars 41–44. Single RH slur to bars 41–44 also viable: **A**^{2}: RH slur extends beyond bar 42, where page ends, without continuation on next page

Bar 42. **F**: no fingering to RH note 1 (cf. bar 41; **A**^{2} as here)

Bar 43. LH staccato dot from **E**, **G**

Bars 43, 58. **A**^{2}, **F**: fingering '5', not '4', to RH notes 4, 10; here by analogy with bar 41 as amended at proof stage

Bar 45. **F**: * at end of bar 46; moved here to bar 45 to avoid blurring

Bars 45–46. **F**: no LH slur in bar 45 at end of system, new system from bar 46 begins with carried-over LH slur; here by analogy with bars 47–48

Bar 46. **F**: additional > between staves LH chord 2 to RH note 11 (redundant, hence removal here)

Bar 47. **F**: Ped. (not present in **A**^{2}) appears ambiguously between LH chord 1 and LH note 2 (here by analogy with beat 2 in bars 55, 56: **G** as here); middle two notes LH chord 3 attached to upstem, not downstem (here by analogy with bar 48; in **A**^{2} unattached to either stem)

Bar 48. * from **G**^{3}, **E**^{3}

Bar 52. Long accent to LH chord 2 as in bars 4, 12

Bar 54. * as in bar 6

Bar 55. **F**: > between LH chords 2 and 3, not long accent to LH chord 2, probably inaccurate implementation of proof emendation (**A**^{2}: > to RH note 7, LH chord 3); here as in bar 56

Bar 56. **F**: > to bar 56 RH note 8 (mislocation in **A**^{2} for note 7, aligned above another > to LH chord 3, replaced at proof stage by long accent to LH chord 2); here as in bar 55

Bar 57. Staccato dot to RH note 5 from **A**^{2} (readable as a light accent), to RH note 11 by analogy

Bar 58. Staccato dots to LH chords 2, 4 from **E**, **G**^{3}

Bar 59. **F**: LH chord 4 includes $b[\flat]^1$ (as in **A**^{2}, left by evident oversight when $b[\flat]$ was added at proof stage); here as in bar 57. Final * from **E**.

Bar 60. **F**: no accent to RH note 1 (cf. surrounding bars; **A**^{2} as here); RH note 7 misprinted as $b[\flat]^2$ (here as corrected by hand in **D**, **S**, as per **A**$^{2)}$

Bars 61–63. **F**: RH slur begins bar 63 RH note 1 (*ad hoc* reading of **A**^{2}: RH slur erroneously omitted in bars 61–62 at end of page, then carried over on new page from bar 63)

Bar 62. **F**: no accent to RH note 1 (cf. bars 57–59, 61; **A**^{2} as here). Accent to RH note 7 by analogy with bar 61.

Bars 62–65. **F**: *poco rall.* from bar 64 RH note 7, ***pp*** at bar 65, both deleted by Chopin in **D** (non-sequitur to preceding *cresc.*); probably unintended remnants from **A**^{2} (which also has ***p*** at bar 63, not *cresc.* _ _ _ from bar 62, and additional slur bar 64 RH note 12 to bar 65 RH note 1, the rhythm of bar 65 RH notes 1–3 ). In bar 65 *delicatiss.* and *smorz.* might thus be regarded as also intended for removal.

Bars 63–65. LH fingering from **D**, which also shows vertical stroke signifying articulation break after bar 65 RH note 1

Bar 65. **F**: no arpeggiation sign (**A**^{2} as here)

Bar 66. **F**: no > to upper staff note 2 (**A**^{2} as here). *Poco rall.* (anticipating ensuing *a tempo*) replaces Chopin's deletion noted above in bar 64. Lower staff fingering from **D**, doubtless signifying left thumb for both $e[\flat]^1$ and $g[\flat]^1$ (cf. '1' fingering to bar 65 RH note 12). Final * from **G**^{3}.

Bar 72. Fingering from **D**

Bar 73. **A**^{2}, **F**: *poco cresc.* ('poco' probably confusion with bar 69, given ***f*** in bar 75, hence reduction here to *cresc.*)

Bars 73–74. LH slurs, long accent to bar 74 LH chord 3 from **E**^{3}

Bars 76–77. **F**: no LH slur over barline (cf. bars 75–76; **A**^{2} as here)

Bar 79. **F**: no ▾ to RH note 1, no LH 𝄽 (**A**^{2} as here)

Bars 83–84. **A**^{2}: LH bar 83 chord 2 to bar 84 chord 1 originally an octave higher, then deleted and rewritten as here on staff underneath, the original notation implying that both hands may originally have been envisaged an octave higher, an option just beyond the compass of most 1830s pianos

No. 6 in E♭ minor

The principal source in this edition is **F**, which shows significant revisions made at proof stage. Reference is made to **A**^{2} to identify engraving inaccuracies or oversights.

Bars 1, 4. **F**: no LH slur (cf. bars 2, 3; **A**^{2} as here)

Bars 1, 5, 9, 13. **F**: no fingering to RH last note (**A**^{2} as here)

Bars 1, 41. **F**: no > to RH note 1 (cf. bar 9; **A**^{2} as here)

Bar 2. **F**: no RH slur (**A**^{2} as here)

Bar 3. **F**: > begins after chord 1 (inaccurate rendering of **A**^{2}: as here), possibly readable as long accent. RH slur from **A**^{2}

(its ends unclear); alternative fingering '*1 3*' respectively to LH notes 2, 3 from **S** (almost overwriting printed '2 4')

Bars 4, 12. Precautionary ♭ to RH note 3 from **G**

Bars 4–6. Fingering to bar 4 RH, bar 6 RH chord 1, with thumb-slide indication from bar 5 RH note 6, by analogy with bars 12, 45–46

Bar 5. **F**: no long accent to RH chord 1 (cf. bar 13; **A**^{2} as here). Precautionary ♭ to LH note 6 from **G**.

Bar 7. Placing of fingering in beat 1 can be read as delineating RH from LH; '1' below lower staff note 8 (not present in **A**^{2}) possibly a misplaced indication for RH (assuming fingering *2* for mid-bar RH $c\flat^1$); traces remain in **F** of '1' above, not below, lower staff notes 1, 3, 5 (evidently relocated as here at proof stage, as in **A**^{2}). **G**: ♮ to lower note upper staff chord 2 (probably an editor's intervention).

Bar 8. **F**: *cresc.* appears between staves, not above RH, preceded by < above LH notes 2–6 (conflicting with < under LH; **A**^{2} as here). **A**^{2}, **F**: no ♭ to LH note 12; here by analogy with bars 7, 9.

Bar 9. **F**: no LH slur (cf. bar 1; roughly drawn in **A**^{2} under LH notes 3–11)

Bar 10. **A**^{2}, **F**: LH slur ends LH note 11 (LH note 12 not present in **A**^{2}); here as in bar 2. RH slur as in bar 2.

Bar 11. **F**: no long accent to RH chord 1 (**A**^{2} as here; see also bars 3, 43)

Bar 12. Fingering from **J**

Bars 12–13. Quaver stem to bar 12 LH note 11 and ensuing tie to bar 13 LH chord 1 *g*♮ by analogy with bars 5–6, 44–45

Bar 13. **F**: no ***f***, no augmentation dot to LH chord 1 (cf. bar 5; **A**^{2} as here)

Bar 15. **F**: ♮ to lower staff note 11, not *f* on beat 2 (**G**, **E** as here); no ♭ to lower staff note 8 (faulty correction at proof stage of lacunae in **A**^{2}, where the only accidentals present are those to upper-staff chord 2 and lower-staff notes 3, 9); here as in bars 47, 48

Bars 16–17. **F**: LH slur extends beyond bar 16, where page ends, without continuation on next page (**A**^{2}: slur ends bar 16 LH note 12)

Bar 17. **F**: fingering '4' to middle note last RH chord overwritten in **S** by '*3*' as here; < ends just before last RH chord (**A**^{2}: upper arm of < ends as here, lower arm extends to bar 18 RH chord 1; here as in bar 19)

Bar 18. **F**: fingering '1 2' respectively to LH notes 10, 11 (not present in **A**^{2}; probably erroneous transposition, though cf. bars 20–21 here by analogy with bar 15 (where *2*, *1* is the only feasible option for the corresponding notes); **Mik** as here

Bar 20. **F**: RH chords 2–3 linked by slur $g\natural^1$–$e[\natural]^1$, not tie $e\natural^1$–$e[\natural]^1$ (misprint of enharmonic respelling at proof stage, the chords notated in **A**^{2} as a single dotted-crotchet chord); no augmentation dot to lower note LH chord 1 (cf. bar 18; **A**^{2} as here)

Bar 21. **F**: ***fp***, not ***fzp***, middle note RH chord 1 stemmed with top note, not bottom note (misreadings of **A**^{2}: as here); no long accent to RH chord 1, no augmentation dot to LH note 1 (**A**^{2} as here)

Bar 22. **F**: no augmentation dot to top note beat 2 RH chord (**A**^{2} as here). > from **A**^{2}.

Bar 23. **F**: no RH slur (**A**^{2} as here). Fingering from **D**; > from **A**^{2}.

Bars 25–26. **F**: LH slur printed under the notes, extending to end of bar 25, where system ends, without subsequent continuation on new system (**A**^{2} as here)

Bar 26. Lower note LH chord 1 from **A**^{2}; it is uncertain if its absence in **F** (see also comment to bars 25–26) results from proof revision or engraver oversight, though the fingering presupposes its presence

Bars 27–28. LH slur from **E**^{3}; RH slur by analogy with bars 25–26

Bar 28. **F**: augmentation dots to RH beat 2 $b[\sharp]^1/d[\sharp]^2$, not present in **A**^{2} but consistent with **A**^{2}, where RH note 12 appears without ♮; RH 𝄾 here instead, as consistent with RH note 12, also by analogy with bar 26

Bar 29. **A**^{2}, **F**: no ♮s to LH chord 1 (cf. bars 30, 31; here as corrected by hand in **S**). Precautionary ♭ to beat 2 RH c^2 from **S**.

Bars 30, 31. Precautionary ♭ to top note RH chord 7 from **G**^{3}

Bars 31–32. **F**: slur beginning bar 31 RH chord 7 ends just beyond barline after bar 32 (**A**^{2}: slur ends bar 32 RH note 12); here by analogy with bars 22, 26, 34, 36, 38

Bar 32. **F**: ***f***, not ***fz*** (misreading of **A**^{2}: as here)

Bar 33. ♭ to middle note RH chord 1 from **G**^{3}

Bars 33–34. **F**: no RH slur (cf. bars 21–22 *et seq.*; **A**^{2} as here)

Bar 34. **F**: traces of erased ♯ to RH note 2, redundant ♭ to bottom note RH chord 7 (vestiges of **A**^{2}:

).

G: no precautionary ♭ to bottom note RH chord 1; **G**^{3} instead adds ♮ (partially reverting to **A**^{2}).

Bars 35–36. **F**: > above bar 35 RH chord 7 (see **A**^{2} variant), > between staves bar 36 RH chord 1 to RH note 4; probably corruption of intended long accent to bar 36 RH chord 1, added at proof stage to replace > in bar 35 (the accent marking the prime dissonance in each source); here by analogy with bars 37–38. **A**^{2}, **F**: ♮ to RH f^1 at bar 35 RH chord 7 possibly implies an assumed $f[\flat]^1$ in **A**^{2} at RH notes 2, 4, thus:

Bar 38. RH beat 2 augmentation dots from **E**

Bars 39–40. **F**: slur beginning bar 39 RH chord 1 extends just beyond barline after bar 39 (**A**^{2}: RH slur extends beyond bar 39, where page ends, without continuation in bar 40); here as in bars 35–38

Bar 40. LH beat 2 slur from **A**^{2}

Bar 42. **F**: erroneous augmentation dot to lower note RH chord 1 instead of tie to RH note 3 (cf. bars 2, 10; misreading of **A**^{2}: as here, tie added by hand in **J**). RH slur from **E**^{3}.

Bar 44. **F**: no augmentation dot to lower note LH chord 1 (cf. bars 4, 12; **A**^{2} as here)

Bar 45. **F**: no augmentation dot to RH lower voice (cf. bars 5, 13; **A**^{2} as here); no fingering to RH note 6 (**A**^{2} as here, also **S**)

Bars 45–46. Bar 46 fingering, along with thumb-slide indication over barline, from **S**

Bar 46. **A**^{2}, **F**: RH chord 1 on single upstem, lower note augmentation dot present only in **A**^{2} (here as in bars 6, 14)

Bar 48. **F**: no >, no augmentation dots to RH chord 1 (cf. bar 47; **A**^{2} as here)

Bar 50. **A**^{2} RH variant: augmentation dots from an earlier deleted version of beat 1 (doubtless overlooked when recopying), the first grace note to sound together with RH/LH lower voice (see also bar 8). Precautionary ♭ to upper note RH chord 1 from **E**, **G**^{3}.

Bars 51–52. Fingering '*1*' to bar 51 lower staff notes 5, 7, 12, to bar 52 semiquaver 1 from **S**

Bars 51–53. Bass ties from **A**^{2}

Bar 52. Slur to lower staff notes 2–7 from **A**^{2}

No. 7 in C major

The principal source in this edition is **F**, which shows significant revisions made at proof stage. Reference is made to **A**^{2} to identify engraving inaccuracies or oversights.

Bar 0. **A**^{2}: tempo indication ~~*Presto*~~ / *Vivace* M.M. ♩. = 88
Bar 2. **F**: no RH slur (cf. bars 1, 3; **A**^{2} as here, also **E**)
Bar 3. *cresc.* from **A**^{2}
Bar 4. **F**: single slur RH chords 1–12 (contradicting dynamics, harmonic motion and LH phrasing: **A**^{2} as here)
Bars 4, 7, 33, 37. **F**: no LH crotchet sustaining stems (cf. bars 2, 6; **A**^{2} as here)
Bars 5, 6, 7, 8, 9, 10, 11. RH slurs from **E**
Bars 5–6. **F**: < ends bar 5 RH chord 12 before system break, new system begins with < starting before bar 6 RH chord 1 (probably a proofing mishap, the intent a single unbroken <, as here and by analogy with bars 1–2; **A**^{2}: lower arm of < extends over barline after bar 5, then separate < under bar 6 RH chords 8–12)
Bar 6. **F**: no staccato LH note 1 (cf. bar 2; **A**^{2}: ▾, as here)
Bar 7. **F**: no > (defining extent of *cresc.*; **A**^{2} as here)
Bar 10. **F**: no > to LH note 3, no ♭ to upper note RH chord 9 (cf. bars 1, 2, 5, 6, 9; **A**^{2} as here)
Bars 10–11, 35–36. **F**: LH slur ends LH note 6 in bars 10, 35, no LH slur in bars 11, 36; **A**^{2}: LH slur initially to bar 2 LH note 6, then extended into bar 3 as in **F**; here by analogy
Bars 11–12. LH mid-bar tie by analogy with bars 3, 36 (where corresponding tie appears only in **F**), ensuing LH slur and LH crotchet sustaining stem by analogy with bars 3–4 (see comment to bars 4, 7, 33, 37)
Bar 13. **A**^{2}, **F**: no augmentation dot to LH minim c^1; here as in bars 5, 34 (also present in **G**)
Bars 14–15. **F**: < ends bar 14 RH chord 12, where page ends, new page begins with < under bar 15 RH chords 1–12 (probably a proofing mishap, the intent a single unbroken < as here, though cf. bar 7; **A**^{2}: < ends bar 14 RH chord 12, bar 15 no dynamics)
Bar 15. **A**^{2}, **F**: no ♯ to upper note RH chord 12; here as in bar 7 (also present in **G**, **E**)
Bar 16. **A**^{2}: ♭ to upper note RH chord 7, not chord 11. Alternative ▾ to LH note 1 from **A**^{2} (see bars 6, 17).
Bar 18. Slur to LH notes 6–7 from **E**
Bar 19. ▾ to LH note 5 from **G**^{1,2}. < > by analogy with bars 17, 21.
Bar 21. **F**: no < > (cf. bars 17, 23; **A**^{2} as here). Staccato dot to LH note 1 from **G** (see bar 23).
Bar 22. **A**^{2}, **F**: staccato dot to LH note 1 (probably slip of the pen, hence removal here)
Bar 23. RH slur from **A**^{2}
Bar 24. **F**: no staccato dot to LH chord 1 (cf. bar 25: **A**^{2} as here)
Bars 24–25. **F**: LH slur ends bar 24 LH chord 4 (despite quaver beam; **A**^{2} as here, latter portion of slur obscured by <)
Bar 25. **F**: lower note RH chord 1 misprinted as e^1 (**A**^{2} as here)
Bar 26. **F**: no LH *fz* (cf. bars 24, 25; **A**^{2} as here). Fingering from **A**^{2}, which also shows '*1*' under '*4*' and '*3*', probably slips of the pen for '*2*'.
Bar 27. **F**: upper note RH chord 10 f^1, not g^1 (misreading of **A**^{2}: as here)
Bar 29. **A**^{2}, **F**: > under RH chords 3–6 (in **A**^{2} readable as long accent); amended by hand in **D** to >, as here
Bars 30, 31. Tie to LH notes 1–2, > from **A**^{2} (the latter possibly readable as long accent: see bar 32)
Bar 33. **F**: no ♮ to lower note RH chord 11 ($d\natural^1$ by default in **A**^{2}, which spells lower note RH chords 5, 6 as $e[\flat]^1$)
Bar 34. **F**: no > to LH note 2 (cf. bars 5, 9, 13; **A**^{2} as here)
Bars 35, 38, 39. Staccato dot to LH note 1 from **G** (see bars 1, 2, 9)
Bar 37. **F**: no > RH chords 7–12 (cf. bars 4, 12; **A**^{2} as here)
Bar 38. **F**: LH beat 1 possibly *ad hoc* repair at proof stage (or engraver's interpretation) of ambiguity in **A**^{2} (where LH beat 1 is aligned as in present variant but misnotated as [music example]; LH variant here by analogy with bars 5, 13, 34). Fingering from **D**.
Bar 40. **F**: no > above LH chord 2 (cf. bar 41; **A**^{2} as here)
Bar 41. **F**: no LH slurs (cf. bar 40; **A**^{2} as here)
Bar 42. **F**: no LH >, no > (cf. bars 40–41; **A**^{2} as here)
Bar 47. **F**: no > (cf. bar 45; **A**^{2} as here). LH slurs, > from **E** (see bar 45). < by analogy with bar 45.
Bars 48, 50. **A**^{2}, **F**: no ♭ to lower note RH chord 11; here by analogy with RH chord 3 (also present in **G** bar 48, **G**, **E** bar 50)
Bars 49–50. **F**: RH/LH slur extends beyond bar 49, ending a system (possibly engraver confusion with system break after bar 48 in **A**^{2}), contradicted in bar 50 by new RH slur as here, new LH slur beginning just after LH chord 1, no ▾ to LH chord 1; here as in **A**^{2} and by analogy with bar 48
Bar 53. **F**: upper note RH chord 6 misprinted as f^1 (**A**^{2} as here)
Bar 56. **F**: no RH ▾ (cf. bars 48, 50; **A**^{2} as here)
Bars 57–58. **F**: no RH slur over barline (**A**^{2} as here, slur partly obscured by adjacent notations)
Bar 58. **F**: ***ff*** appears at bar 59 (implausibly late), not bar 58 RH/LH chord 2 (**A**^{2} as here, also implied by **D** variant)

No. 8 in F major

Principal source: **A**^{2}. **F** is unviable as principal source because of endemic omissions and misprints. Its textural revisions, shown here as variants, are best viewed in the context of **A**^{2}.

Phrasing. **A**^{2}: many RH slurs are drawn hastily or approximately, leaving discontinuities or ambiguities notably over system breaks: these are remedied here partly by analogy with bars 16–23, 33–34 (where **A**^{2} shows slur ends retouched by Chopin to correct analogous discontinuities of pen stroke), and as in **F** in bars 62, 67, 93–94. (**F** otherwise leaves the discontinuities mostly unaddressed.)

Pedalling. Pedalling in round brackets is from **F** unless noted otherwise. Some suspect pedalling in **F** is ignored.

All fingering in italics is from **F** unless noted otherwise.

Bar 0. **F**: time signature **C**. Fingering from **D**.
Bar 1. *veloce* from **F** (where it appears illogically against LH chord 1; **G** as here)
Bar 4. **F**: additional > to LH note 5
Bar 8. LH fingering from **D**
Bars 8–9, 22–23, 68–69. *cresc.*, ***f*** from **F**
Bar 12. **A**^{2}: no ♮ to top note LH chord 1 (here by analogy with RH and bar 11). Variant from **F**, **G**, **E**: replacement of LH chord 1 and ensuing 𝄽 (as in **A**^{2}) by ▬ raises a query of why (e.g. because the chord was omitted or misprinted in proofs for **F**^{1}?); see reciprocal passages at bars 27, 71–72, 86–87, also Etude 4 at bars 48, 49. Fingering to RH note 2 from **G**^{1,2}, **E** (cf. bar 11), to RH note 14 from **F**.
Bar 13. *cresc.* from **F**
Bar 14. Fingering above RH note 2 from **D**
Bars 15, 19. ✻ by analogy with bar 5 (see also bars 33, 65; **F** instead has ✻ under RH note 4 in bars 16, 20)
Bar 19. **A**^{2}: no ♮ to LH beat 2 grace note *B* (cf. bars 1, 3 *et seq.*; **F** as here)
Bars 20, 22. Staccato dot to LH chord 1 from **F**
Bars 23–24, 69–70. LH staccato dots by analogy with bars 9–10
Bars 28–29. Slur beginning bar 28 LH note 2 from **F**, which omits continuation in bar 29 on new page (**E** as here)

Bars 30, 34. LH slurs from **E**
Bar 32. Staccato dot to LH chord 1 from **F**^{1}
Bar 37. **A**^{2}: first RH slur begins under RH note 3 (**F**: separate slurs RH notes 1–4, 5–8)
Bar 40. ***f*** from **F**
Bar 41. Staccato dot to LH from **E**
Bar 43. ♯ to LH note 2 from **S** (**G**: ♮ instead)
Bar 47. **A**^{2}: no ♮ to RH notes 2, 6 (cf. bars 48, 49, 50: **F** as here)
Bars 47–48, 49–50. Broken lines after *cresc.* based partly on **A**^{2} (roughly drawn line under bar 48 RH notes 4–6; see bars 49–50), partly on **F** (broken line after *cresc.* bar 47 RH note 16 to bar 49 RH note 12, no *cresc.* bar 49)
Bars 47, 49. **A**^{2}: augmentation dot to upper note LH chord 2 instead of ensuing tie and bottom note LH chord 3 (here renotated for clarity; **F**: as **A**^{2} without augmentation dot). ❊ from **F** (appearing there respectively at bar 48 LH note 2, bar 50 note 1; adjusted here for clarity, as in **G**).
Bar 48. Fingering '5' to RH note 12 from **G**, **E** (see bar 50)
Bar 51. Arpeggiation sign, > to LH chord 1 from **F** (where no > appears to LH chord 2); LH slur from **E**, **G**^{3}
Bar 52. *cresc.* from **F**; ensuing broken line by analogy with bars 47–48, 49–50 (see also bar 53)
Bars 53–54. **F**: 𝆮 appears under bar 53 LH 𝄾 (no space above or under LH note 2), no ❊; here by analogy with bars 55–56 and as in **G**
Bars 54–55. Broken line after *cresc.* implied by erased ***f*** in **A**^{2} at bar 55 RH/LH note 1 (it is unlikely that *cresc.* was intended to continue through bar 55)
Bar 55. LH slurs, precautionary ♮ to RH note 3 from **F**
Bar 57. **A**^{2}: no ♭ to LH note 15 (**F**^{2,3} as here)
Bar 58. **A**^{2}: no ♭ to LH note 14 (cf. bar 59; **F** as here)
Bar 59. **A**^{2}: no ♯ to RH note 1, no ♮ to RH note 6 (cf. bar 60; **F** as here); no ♮ to LH note 15 (**F**^{2,3} as here)
Bar 61. LH staccato dots by analogy with bars 63, 65
Bars 62, 64, 66, 68. LH staccato dots by analogy with bars 2, 4 *et seq.*
Bars 62, 66. **A**^{2}: bar 62 LH slur originally extended to LH note 5, then erased from LH note 4 onward (**F** as here); cf. bar 66
Bar 64. LH slur from **E**
Bar 67. Staccato dot to LH note 4 from **G**
Bar 71. ⟩ from **E** (see bars 72, 73); LH 𝄾 (under RH note 13) from **G**; ❊ from **E**, **G**^{3}
Bar 73. ***f*** appears only in **A**^{2}; the context of the preceding ***ff*** suggests ***f***[***z***]
Bars 74–75. **A**^{2}: new system at bar 75 begins with carried-over RH slur, but no beginning to it in bar 74 (**F**: slur begins bar 75 RH note 1); here as implied by > to bar 74 RH chord 4
Bar 75. ❊ from **E**, **G**^{3}
Bars 76–77. Lower LH tie over barline by analogy with bars 80–81
Bar 78. **A**^{2}: no ♭ to RH note 15 (cf. RH note 6: **F** as here). Fingering to RH note 16 from **S**.
Bars 78–79, 79–80. LH cross-bar ties by analogy with bars 80–81 (see also bars 76–77), implied by surrounding articulation (especially upbeat >s), which otherwise makes little sense
Bar 79. **A**^{2}: no ♭ to LH chord 1 (cf. bar 75; **F** as here); no ♭ to RH note 8 (**F** as here)
Bar 80. **A**^{2}: no ♭ to RH note 2 (**F**, **E**: ♮, probably misprint of ♭ added at proof stage); here by analogy with bar 76 (and as in **G**^{3})
Bar 81. *sempre legatissimo* from **F**; fingering to RH notes 1, 3, 13–15 from **S**
Bar 83. Fingering to RH note 5 from **S**
Bars 83–84, 85–86. LH slur over barline from **F**
Bar 84. **A**^{2}: LH chord 1 on single upstem, durations as here; **F**: bottom 2 notes semibreves, not minims
Bar 88. **F**: > to RH note 13
Bar 89. Staccato dot, arpeggiation sign to LH chord 1 from **F**
Bar 90. **A**^{2}: fingering '5', '4' respectively to RH notes 2, 3 (doubtless erroneous transposition: cf. bar 89; **F** as here)
Bar 94. **A**^{2}: no 𝄢 after LH note 1 (**F** as here), erroneous c^2 in RH chord 3. d^2 in second chord of RH variant possibly unintended remnant from revisions at proof stage (congesting the variant's otherwise clarified RH line e^2–f^2–g^2).
Bar 95. **A**^{2}: minim stem to RH bottom note (remnant of earlier version). **G**: additional f^1 in LH chord 1.

No. 9 in F minor

The principal source in this edition is **F**, which shows significant revisions made at proof stage. Reference is made to **A**^{2} to identify engraving inaccuracies or oversights.

Suggested filiation. **A**^{1} probably served as preparatory draft for **A**^{2}; its LH, often notated in shorthand form, is left blank in bars 49–63, the RH upper octave not present in bars 45–48.

A = A^{1,2}

Ornaments. **A**^{1}: ⁓ to RH $d[\flat]^2$ in bars 2, 3, 6 (without staccato dot except in bar 6); ***tr*** equivalently in bar 7; bars 9–15 indicated as repeating bars 1–7; no ⁓ in bars 38, 39. **A**^{2}: ⁓̸ (probable error for ⁓) instead of staccato dot to RH $d[\flat]^2$ in bars 2, 3; ***tr*** equivalently in bars 6, 7; bars 38–39 conversely with staccato dot, not ⁓; bar 42 RH beginning  (traces also remain of the same *Vorschlag*, erased, before RH note 3 in bars 3 and 11, and of erased ⁓̸ to bar 10 RH note 2). **F** shows traces of the final **A**^{2} readings, evidently amended as here at proof stage. **Tel**: ⁓ as in **A**^{1} bars 2, 3, 7 (not bar 6), as here in bars 38, 39. See also comment to bar 64.

All fingering in italics is from **D** unless noted otherwise.

Bar 1. **A**^{1}: tempo indication *Agitato*; **A**^{2}: ~~*Presto*~~ / *All° molto agitato* 𝅗𝅥. = 92
Bars 2, 26, 39, 44. **F**: no LH slurs (cf. bars 1, 8, 21–25, 37, 40); **A** as here bar 2, **A**^{2} as here bars 26, 39; bar 44 by analogy with bar 8
Bars 3–6, 9–14, 38, 41–42. LH slurs from **A**^{1} (fully notated in bars 3–4, later bars indicated as repetitions or by 'come sopra')
Bar 4. **F**: no ***fz*** (cf. bars 20, 48; **A**^{2} as here)
Bar 5. ***p*** by reference to dynamics in bars 2–3, 6–8 (see also bars 1, 9, 17, 21)
Bar 8. **F**: *Ritard* (*sic*) and *cresc.* each begin just before RH/LH note 3 (i.e. barely affecting RH; **A**^{2} placing as here, but with 'rittenuto' [*sic*], not *rit.*). **A**^{2}, **F**: LH note 9 *f*, not *a*[♭] (doubtless slip of the pen: cf. LH note 3, also bars 16, 44; **A**^{1} as here).
Bars 9, 45. Precautionary ♮ to LH note 2 from **G**^{3}
Bar 15. Staccato dots to RH notes 4–6 from **A**^{1} (reprise of bar 7), **G** (in **A**^{2} slur ends RH note 4)
Bars 17–18. **F**: RH slur begins bar 18 RH note 1 at start of new system (in **A**^{2} it begins above barline beginning bar 18); amended by Chopin in **D** to begin as here (see bar 21)
Bars 20–21. Bar 21 lower note RH chord 1 from **A**^{1}, which in bars 20–21 gives RH as  (augmentation dot to upper note of octave chord only, slur tailing off just after it, ***pp*** not entirely clear). **F**: RH tie from bar 20 RH note 2 extends to barline ending system, without continuation on next system (bar 21 RH slur as here); **A**^{2}: roughly drawn tie or slur beginning under bar 20 RH note 2 ends before LH note 12, preceding the end of a page, without continuation on new page (bar 21 RH slur

as per present variant). (Tie and slur are thus explicitly separate in both **A**^{1} and **A**^{2}; **E**: single slur bar 20 RH note 2 to bar 22 RH note 1.)

Bar 23. **F**: redundant staccato dot to RH note 1 (not present in **A**, contradicts tie, hence removal here)

Bars 24, 25. **F**: no ▾ to RH note 1 (cf. equivalent accentuation in bars 4, 12, 20, 40, 48; **A**^{2} as here)

Bar 25. **F**: ***f***, not *forte* (misleadingly suggesting an autonomous dynamic); **A**^{2} as here

Bar 27. Precautionary ♮ to LH note 10 from **A**^{1}

Bar 28. **F**: *ottava* line ends prematurely, with 'Loco' above RH chord 1 (here as corrected by Chopin in **D**, **S**, as per **A**); no ⟩ (cf. surrounding ***ff***, ***f***; **A**^{2} as here)

Bars 33, 34. Slur to RH chords/notes 6–7 from **E**

Bars 33, 35. **A**^{1}: ***ff***, not ***f***

Bar 35. **F**: no augmentation dots to RH chord 6 (**A** as here)

Bar 36. Final ✽ from **E**, **G**^{3}

Bar 45. **F**: no staccato dot to RH chord 4 (cf. chords 1–3; **A**^{2} as here). Fingering '3' to LH note 2 as implied by '4' to LH note 8 (after '4' in bar 37).

Bar 48. **F**: no long accent to RH chord 1 (cf. bars 16, 20, also bars 4, 12, 40; **A**^{2} as here)

Bar 50. First ✽ from **G**, **E**

Bar 57. RH staccato dots from **G** (see bars 29–31, 58–59), first dot also present in **A**^{2} (which slurs RH chords 2–3); > to RH chord 3 by analogy with bar 58

Bar 61. **F**: ***f***, not ***ff*** (cf. bar 63; **A**^{2} as here; see also comment to bars 33, 35). Staccato dot to RH chord 6 from **A**^{2}.

Bars 61, 62. Slur to RH beat 2 from **E**

Bar 64. **F**: no augmentation dot to RH note 7 (**A** as here). **A**: RH note 7 preceded by grace note $a[\flat]^1$ (answering analogous grace-note octave $a[\flat]^1/a[\flat]^2$ written, then deleted, in **A**^{1} in bar 63); in **F**, spacing and untidiness on the staff suggest the grace note was removed at proof stage (possibly to echo bar 63 exactly; cf. bars 29–36, 57–62).

Bars 66–67. LH slur from **A**^{2}

Bar 67. **F**: no staccato dot to RH (cf. LH; **A**^{2} as here). RH/LH rests possibly *ad hoc* correction at proof stage of missing RH/LH 𝄾 in **A**^{2} (cf. **A**^{1}: RH/LH ♩. 𝄽 𝄾), though they continue hemiola pattern of bars 65–66.

No. 10 in A♭ major

Principal source: **A**^{2}. **F** is unviable because of endemic omissions and misprints; some evident revisions in **F**, shown here as variants, also make sense only if seen in the context of **A**^{2}.

Bar 0. **F**: LH 𝄽 (as in **A**^{2}) under RH ♪ (**G**: LH 𝄾); it is not clear whether the RH duration represents a revision at proof stage or a misprint (the engraver possibly confused by a crotchet upbeat in 12/8 metre, the fingering '1' from **A**^{2} either overlooked or deemed inapplicable to the shortened upbeat)

Bars 1–8, 17–20. **F**: traces appear in reprints of the additional RH >s present in **A**^{2} in bars 1–4, 6–8, 17–20, attesting to their removal at proof stage; in bar 5 these traces erroneously continue the pattern of accents from **A**^{2} in bars 1–4. If the deletions at proof stage were partly aimed at rectifying that error, ironically they embed its effect by cancelling the differentiation of accentuation in **A**^{2} between bars 4 and 5 (an element ostensibly fundamental to this etude); Chopin perhaps considered the RH two-note slurs in bars 1–2 sufficient to convey the differentiation. **F**: >s remain present to bar 4 RH note 8, bar 8 RH note 1 and bar 20 RH chord 8, doubtless in error (contradicting the surrounding pattern), hence their removal here from the RH variant.

Bar 2. Precautionary ♭ to RH note 1 from **G** (and **F** at equivalent bars 6, 56, 70); two-note RH slurs beats 3, 4 from **G**, **E**

Bars 3, 6. **A**^{2}, **F**: LH note 10 has open notehead (i.e. as minim, not crotchet) for sustained voice; corrected here to avoid harmonic clash on ensuing beat (cf. bar 4 LH note 4, bar 7 LH notes 4, 10)

Bar 7. **A**^{2}: no ♮ to LH note 11 (cf. RH chord 12; **F** as here). **A**^{2}, **F**: LH note 5 d^1, not f^1, preceded in **A**^{2} by redundant ♮; this, along with d^1's disruption of rising thumb line and resulting parallel octaves with RH (from a doubled leading note), suggests an error of parablepsis (beat 1 inadvertently copied twice); here by analogy with bar 16 (see also bars 14, 60).

Bars 7–8. Pedalling from **F**

Bar 8. Precautionary ♭ to RH note 3 from **G**^{3}

Bar 12. **A**^{2}: no ♭ to LH note 8 (cf. bar 4; **F** as here)

Bar 13. **A**^{2}, **F**: no ♮ to lower note RH chord 6 (**F**: ♮ to RH note 11 instead); here as in bars 1, 5, 59, also **G**^{3} (see comments to bar 55, bar 69)

Bars 15–20, 23–26, 29–32. Second ✽ in bar 16 from **G**, **E**, other pedalling from **F** (where some pedal changes appear a note earlier, Ped. positioned to left of bass beam)

Bar 16. **F**: LH note 5 g^1, not $b[\flat]^1$ (probably misreading)

Bar 23. ♭ to RH note 9 by analogy with bars 35, 39 (see comment to bars 35, 39; **G**: ♮ to upper note chord 10 instead)

Bar 25. Precautionary ♭ to lower note RH chord 8 from **F** (cf. bars 40, 64)

Bar 26. Precautionary ♮ to LH note 4 from **G**^{3}

Bar 27. Last RH slur from **F**

Bar 28. Fingering, final ✽ from **F**; slurs RH note 1 to RH chord 6 by analogy with bar 27

Bars 28–29. **A**^{2}: deleted *cres.* beginning bar 28 LH note 8; the deletion possibly distracted Chopin from indicating dynamics in bar 29 (cf. bars 17, 33; ***pp*** or ***f*** feasible here)

Bar 30. **A**^{2}: crotchet upstem to RH note 7 (no discernible musical purpose, possibly an abandoned attempt at stemming the group upwards)

Bars 35, 39. **A**^{2}: no ♭ to RH note 9 (**F** as here; **G**: ♮ to bar 35 upper note chord 10 instead, bar 39 as here); see comment to bar 23

Bar 37. **A**^{2}: no ♭ to LH notes 1, 2 (cf. bars 25, 40, where equivalent ♭s are part of key signature); **F** as here LH note 1 (**G**, **E** as here both notes)

Bar 38. Precautionary ♮ to RH note 9 from **F**

Bars 39–42. Final ✽ in bar 42 from **E**, **G**^{3}, other pedalling from **F**

Bar 41. **A**^{2}: no ♮ to RH note 7, upper note RH chord 8 (cf. RH note 1 bars 41, 42; **F** as here RH note 7). Precautionary ♮ to LH note 4 from **F**.

Bar 43. **A**^{2}: *ottava* line begins prematurely, making RH note 7 an octave too high (**F** as here)

Bars 43, 45. Fingering from **F**

Bar 49. Precautionary ♮ to top note LH chord 1, ✽ from **F**

Bar 52. **A**^{2}, **F**: no augmentation dots to LH chord 3; here by analogy with LH chord 1, also bars 51, 53 (**G**, **E** as here)

Bar 55. **A**^{2}, **F**: ♮ to d^2 at RH note 11, not lower note RH chord 6; here by analogy with bars 1, 5, 59 (where ♮ appears at both places in **A**^{2}); see comments to bar 13, bar 69

Bars 61–66, 68–70. First ✽ in bar 64 from **G**, **E**, other pedalling from **F** (where some mid-bar pedal changes appear a note early, probably because of restricted space)

Bar 62. **A**^{2}: lower note RH chord 10 not entirely clear, probably $a[\flat]^2$ amended to $b[\flat]^2$ (emendation possibly read conversely by engraver of **F**, as per variant here)

Bar 63. > by analogy with bars 26, 38 (also envisageable in bars 65, 66, 67 as in bars 41, 42)

Bar 64. Precautionary ♭ to RH chord 8 by analogy with bar 25; **E** variant possibly derived from analogy with bar 40

Bars 67. ♭ to LH note 10 appears only in **A²** (this bar very cramped in **F**)

Bar 68. **A²**: no accidentals in this bar (which breaks system in mid-bar); **F** as here

Bar 69. **A²**, **F**: ♮ to d^3 at RH note 11, not lower note RH chord 6; here by analogy with bars 1, 5, 59 (see comments to bar 13, bar 55)

Bar 76. **A²**, **F**: top note RH chord 8 minim, tied directly to bar 77 $a[\flat]^1$; here as metrically correct

No. 11 in E♭ major

Principal source: **A²** (in which bars 10–15 are indicated as reprise of bars 2–7, with only RH notes of bar 10 written out). **F** is unviable because of endemic omissions and inaccuracies; among the variants from **F** shown here, a few reverse revisions visible on **A²**.

Arpeggiation. **A²**: no arpeggiation signs to either hand bars 9, 27–32, 36, 39–43; to RH bars 10, 26, 35, 38; to LH bars 19, 23–24, 29, 37–38, 50–51; or to bar 22 RH chord 6, bar 23 RH chord 5, bar 29 RH chord 1, bar 37 RH chord 6; here by analogy with surrounding bars or chords (also present in **F** in some of these bars)

Articulation. **D**: vertical lines indicating articulation breaks after RH chord 1 in bars 1, 2, 3, 6, 7 (despite phrasing), 9, 10, 13, 14, 15, 21, 22, 23, 25. In bars 5, 13, 26, 28, 30, 31, 32, 35, 38 the RH staccato dot in **A²** might be read as a carelessly written ▾.

Phrasing. **A²** shows some imprecision in the notation of RH slurs. Slurs ending here at RH note 1 in bars 5, 13, 27, 37, 44, 45, 46 and 47 end in **A²** ambiguously above the preceding barline, mostly pointing towards the ensuing RH chord; here by analogy with slurs in **A²** that end clearly at RH chord 1 in bars 19, 21, 25, 26, 29, 30, 31 and 32. In bar 6 first slur ends in **A²** high between RH chords 3 and 4 (here in relation to ensuing RH slur; bar 14 by analogy, indicated in **A²** as a reprise of bar 6; **F**: bar 6 first slur ends RH chord 6, where system ends; new system in bar 7 begins with carried-over RH slur; in bar 14 slur beginning RH chord 2 continues unbroken through bar 15). In bar 16 **A²**, **F** omit to complete RH slur carried past bar 15; here by analogy with bars 19, 21, 24 *et seq*. In bar 35 slur in **A²** ends after RH chord 6, new slur in bar 36 begins just before RH chord 2 (**F**: slur break over barline; see bars 3–4; here by melodic logic, to avoid new phrase beginning with repeated note). **A²**: no slur in bar 42, new system from bar 43 begins with carried-over RH slur; here by harmonic logic from bar 42 chord 6.

Bar 2. Precautionary ♭ to middle note RH chord 1 from **D**

Bars 3, 11. **A²**: Ped. at bar 3 RH/LH chord 1 (bar 11 indicated as reprise), contradicting harmony, probably inadvertent repetition by rote from bar 2, not repeated in bar 35, hence removal here

Bar 4. **F**: LH chord 1 includes $e[\flat]$ (probably misprint; not present in bars 11, 36)

Bars 5, 9, 13. ***p*** bar 5 from **ZR** (see bar 1, also *cresc.* bars 3, 4); bars 9, 13 by analogy

Bars 6, 14. **A²**, **F**: ✻ just after bar LH chord 6 (in **A²** written only in bar 6, bar 14 indicated as reprise); here by analogy with phrasing (see general comment above concerning phrasing)

Bar 8. **A²**: no cancelling ♮ to middle note RH chord 4, top note LH chord 4 (cf. bar 4; **F** as here)

Bar 9. ✻ from **F**

Bars 15, 39. LH variant from bar 7 also envisageable here (avoiding parallel fifths; **F** as here)

Bar 16. LH staccato dot from **G**, **E** (see bar 8)

Bar 20. Analogy with bar 18 suggests that top note LH chords 5, 6 may have been intended as $a[\flat]^1$, not f^1 (avoiding parallel octaves into bar 21)

Bar 24. **A²**, **F**: no ♭s to RH/LH chord 6 (cf. bar 23; **D** as here)

Bar 26. Precautionary ♭ to middle note RH chord 1 from **F**

Bar 27. Precautionary ♭ to bottom note RH chord 2 from **G³**, to top note LH chord 5 from **F**. ***p*** by analogy with bars 25, 29 (cf. bars 26, 28).

Bar 30. **E**: ♭ to top note RH chord 5

Bar 31. Precautionary ♮ to top note LH chord 5 from **F**

Bar 32. **A²**: no ♮ to top note RH chord 3 (cf. bar 29: **F** as here). **F¹**: no precautionary ♮ to middle note RH chord 5; **F²,³** have ♮♭ (♭ overprinting the arpeggiation sign), probably a botched correction, one symbol intended to replace the other (either is viable, though ♮ more plausible). Precautionary ♭ to top note LH chord 1 from **G**, **E**; final ✻ from **E**, **G³**.

Bar 33. Staccato dot to RH/LH chord 1 from **F**

Bars 33, 34. ✻ from **E**, bar 34 Ped. from **F**

Bar 36. **A²**: no ♮ to g^2 RH chord 4, no ♭ to a^2 RH chord 5 (cf. bar 4; **F** as here)

Bar 37. Staccato dot to LH note 1 from **F**

Bar 38. **A²**, **F**: no ♭s to penultimate RH chord; here as in bars 6, 14 (**G**, **E** as here)

Bar 40. **A²**: no ♮ to middle note RH chord 6, top note LH chord 6 (cf. bar 41; **F** as here)

Bar 41. Precautionary ♮ to bottom note LH chord 4 from **F**

Bar 44. Staccato dot to LH note 1 from **E**

Bars 44–47. Added pedalling by analogy with bars 25–28 (**F**: ✻ at end of bar 45)

Bar 45. Precautionary ♮ to bottom note RH chord 2 from **G³**

Bar 46. **A²**: no ♭ to bottom note RH chord 2 (cf. bar 44; **D** as here). Variant from **D** (in Chopin's hand, with slur over last three chords readable as triplet bracket) might be regarded as a compositional correction, answering bar 27.

Bar 47. Precautionary ♮ to bottom note RH chord 2 from **D**

Bars 47–49. RH slurs, staccato dot to bar 48 RH chord 1 by analogy with bars 45–47, also bar 16; single slur bar 47 RH chord 2 to bar 49 RH chord 1 also viable in relation to bar 48 beaming

Bar 48. **A²**: faint trace of erased $e[\flat]^3$ in RH chord 2 (see variant from **F**, **G**, **E**); LH chord 1 beamed together with LH chords 2–6 (impractical to print; here by analogy with bar 16; **F** as here).

Bars 48, 49. **A²**: no ♮ to top note RH chord 4 (**F²,³** as here)

Bar 49. **A²**: LH chord 3 includes deleted d^1 (not present in bar 48); LH chord 5 untidily written, c^1 unclear (possibly overlooked by engraver); cf. variants from **F**, **G**, **E**

Bars 50, 51. Precautionary ♭ to middle note LH chord 5 from **G**

Bar 52. **F**: ***f*** just after RH/LH chord 2 (close spacing between RH/LH suggests that *sotto voce*, < were never engraved). Staccato dot to RH chord 1 from **F**.

Bars 52–53. *Ottava* beginning bar 52 RH chord 6 from **ZR**, also in **G**, where it also appears less plausibly above LH (it was not Chopin's habit to notate *ottava* above 𝄢); in **ZR** *8*‾ ‾ ‾ was initially pencilled just above RH, then over-pencilled in orange for both hands (possibly copied from her additional **G** exemplar). Repetition of tessitura either before or after the chords in question is unavoidable here, whichever octave is used.

No. 12 in C minor

Principal source: **A**^{2}. The issues with **F** in Etudes 10 and 11 also apply to Etude 12.

Fingering in italics is from **D** as follows: bars 6, 12, 18–19, 41, 57, 79–80; bar 7 LH notes 1–2; bar 25 LH note 2; upper fingering '*1*' to bar 40 LH notes 4, 7; bar 73 LH notes 5, 7, 9, 11, 15; bar 74 LH notes 4, 10, 14 (see also comment to bar 25). All other fingering in italics is from **F**.

Bar 4. > to LH note 9 from **F**

Bar 5. ▾ to RH chord 1, staccato dot to LH note 1 by analogy with bar 45

Bars 1–6. >s could be read as long accents (less so in analogous bars 41–43)

Bars 7–9. **A**^{2}: RH slur beginning bar 7 extends just beyond bar 8, where system ends, without subsequent completion on new system

Bars 10–11, 12–13, 20–21, 22–23. RH cross-bar slur in bars 10–11 from **E**, in bars 12–13, 22–23 from **F** (where equivalent slur also appears to bars 23–24, probably in error for bars 20–21 a system above; cf. bars 11–12, 13–14 *et seq.*); bars 20–21 here by analogy

Bar 12. ⟩ between staves from **F**

Bar 18. *dim.* from **F**

Bars 18, 58. **A**^{2}, **F**: no precautionary ♮ to LH note 1 (here by analogy with bar 75, also in **G**^{3}). **A**^{2}: no ♮ to LH note 8 (**F** as here).

Bar 20. *sotto voce* from **F**

Bar 25. **F**: fingering to LH notes 2–3 erroneously transposed as '*2 3*'; here as corrected in **D** at LH note 2, in **G**, **E** both notes

Bars 25–26. **A**^{2}: additional slurs to bar 25 LH notes 6–9, LH note 15 to bar 26 LH note 1 (written under present slurs, ostensibly contradicting them, hence removal here)

Bars 25–27. RH slur from **E**

Bar 26. Precautionary ♮ to LH note 3 from **F**

Bar 27. **A**^{2}: no ♮ to *a*[♮]^2 RH chord 3 (**F** as here). **F**: LH ⟨ extends to middle of bar; LH note 7 as here, LH note 8 semiquaver, not demisemiquaver (no trace of an effaced beam, suggesting engraver error rather than proof emendation; **G**, **E**: both notes undotted semiquavers).

Bar 28. Middle note RH chord from **F**

Bar 30. **A**^{2}, **F**: LH slur broken between LH notes 4 and 5; here by analogy with bar 32

Bars 30, 32. **A**^{2}: rhythm of RH chords 2–3 probably intended to mitigate parallel ninths with LH; **F**: rhythm  instead in bar 30,  [*sic*] in bar 32 (layout of **F** suggests engraving error rather than proof emendation, as stem lengths and beam position, notably in bar 32, leave insufficient space for demisemiquaver beam)

Bars 33–34, 34–35. RH cross-bar slur bars 34–35 from **F**; RH bars 33–34 by analogy

Bar 34. **F**: RH chord 3 misprinted as , intent undoubtedly as in RH variant (as per **G**, **E**, except precautionary ♭ to *a*[♭]^2 appears only in **G**^{1,2})

Bar 35. **A**^{2}: no ♭ to LH note 7 (cf. bars 33, 34, also bar 36 LH note 5; **F** as here)

Bar 41. Upper note LH chord 1 from **F**

Bar 43. > to LH notes 4, 8, 12 from **F**

Bars 43, 45. Staccato dot to LH note 1 from **E**

Bar 44. **A**^{2}: LH slur fades out above LH note 9 (cf. bar 42; **F** as here). LH >s from **G**^{3}.

Bars 50–51. ⟨ beginning bar 50 RH chord 1 from **F**

Bars 52, 55, 56, 60. RH slur beat 2 in bars 56, 60 from **F**, in bar 52 based on **F** (where slur begins RH chord 2), in bar 55 by analogy. These replace slurs in **A**^{2} over each RH triplet group signifying triplet brackets, the one over bar 55 RH chords 5–7 retained in **F**.

Bar 53. LH slur from **E**

Bar 55. **A**^{2}, **F**: no cancelling ♭s to RH chord 6; here by analogy with bar 15 (also present in **G**)

Bars 57–58. **A**^{2}: LH slur extends beyond bar 57, where system ends, without subsequent continuation on new system; here as slur end bar 18 (**F**: slur ends bar 57 LH note 16)

Bar 62. Each ⟨ ⟩ from **G**^{3}

Bar 64. ⟩ to LH notes 5–7 from **F**

Bar 66. ⟨ from **F**

Bar 68. Precautionary ♮ to LH note 3 from **F**

Bars 69–70. RH slur based on **D** (pencilled by Chopin over bar 69, extending beyond barline at end of system, without subsequent continuation in bar 70; here by analogy with bar 67 and in relation to bar 71)

Bar 70. Beat 2 LH slur from **F**

Bars 71–72. **A**^{2}: top note bar 72 RH chord 1 written blotchily over an illegible erasure ('mi' written to its left as clarification); RH phrasing, along with extent of arpeggiation sign, implies RH tie over barline as here. **F** (RH variant): arpeggiation sign as in **A**^{2}; phrasing implies extension to top note, as here (unless chord is tied over from bar 71).

Bar 73. Staccato dot to LH note 1 from **F**

Bars 73–77. **A**^{2}: separate LH slurs bar 73 LH notes 2–15 (at end of system), bar 74 LH notes 6–16 (on new system), bars 75–76 (**F**: as **A**^{2} except bar 74 LH notes 1–16); redrawn by Chopin in **D** as here

Bar 75. **A**^{2}: no ♯ to LH note 2, no ♮ to LH note 8 (cf. bars 18, 58, 76; **F** as here; **G**^{3}: ♮ also to LH note 5, doubtless by erroneous analogy with RH)

Bars 77–78. **A**^{2}, **F**: LH slur extends beyond bar 77, where system ends, without subsequent continuation on new system (here by analogy with bars 1–2)

Bars 79–80. **A**^{2}: LH slur peters out above bar 79 LH note 11 (cf. bars 1–2; **F** as here)

Bars 80–81. **A**^{2}, **F**: RH slur ends at barline after bar 80; here by analogy with bars 78–79

Bar 82. **A**^{2}: no ♭ to RH/LH notes 7, 15 (cf. bar 81; **F** as here bar 82 RH/LH note 7)

Bar 83. **A**^{2}: RH chord 1 originally with *g*, not *f* (see bar 80, also bar 27), possibly explaining RH articulation; ***fff*** appears between RH chord 2 and barline (intent probably as here, though feasibly readable for bar 84). **F**: no RH slur, no ***fff***; **D**: ***ff*** pencilled above upper staff.

Bar 84. **F**: staccato dots, not ▾s, above RH chords 1, 2. **ZR**: ***fff*** pencilled under lower staff.

THE COMPLETE CHOPIN

— A NEW CRITICAL EDITION —

Editor-in-Chief: John Rink

Series Editors: Jim Samson, Jean-Jacques Eigeldinger, Christophe Grabowski

BALLADES
Edited by Jim Samson (EP7531)

ETUDES Op. 25
Edited by Roy Howat (EP73228)

IMPROMPTUS
Edited by Christophe Grabowski and John Irving (EP71906)

NOCTURNE Op. 9 No. 2
Edited by Christophe Grabowski (EP73577a)

PRÉLUDES
Edited by Jean-Jacques Eigeldinger (EP7532)

RONDOS
Edited by David Rowland (EP72781)

TROIS NOUVELLES ETUDES
Edited by Roy Howat (EP73229)

WALTZES
Edited by Christophe Grabowski (EP7575)

PIANO CONCERTO No. 1
Edited by John Rink (EP7529)

PIANO CONCERTO No. 2
Edited by John Rink (EP71919)

PUBLISHED BY FABER MUSIC
fabermusic.com